Centre for Theology and Public Issues
The University of Edinburgh

Occasional Paper No 45

The Sorrows of Young Men
Exploring their increasing risk of Suicide

Edited by Andrew Morton and Jim Francis

Price £ 5

© Authors

Published by
Centre for Theology and Public Issues
New College
The University of Edinburgh
Mound Place
Edinburgh
EH1 2LU

Occasional Paper No 45

ISBN No. 1 870126 43 2
First Published 2000

Printed by Pace Print (Edinburgh) Ltd
Tel: 0131 667 0737   Fax: 0131 668 1887
Email: paceprintltd@netscapeonline.co.uk

Table of Contents

Foreword

This important conference took place in November 1999, the year in which the first Parliament in Scotland for nearly 300 years became a reality, heralding a new era in our country's development. It is right that, in these exciting times, we should seek ways of communicating the promise of new and better things to everyone in the country. However, it is a sad fact that the rate of suicide amongst young men in Scotland has risen at an alarming rate over the past three decades. The Conference and the set of papers which make up this volume seek to address this issue and the underlying factors in relation to a vital group in our country - young men who, for whatever reason, feel down about their lives, stressed, excluded, and undervalued. Whether as individuals or as communities, it takes courage to face up to uncomfortable and disquieting realities, which reflect on our collective health and well-being; and I commend the organisers and participants in the Conference for their active concern.

We in the Scottish Executive are totally committed to taking steps that improve the prospects for young people in Scotland. We want a good start for every young Scot, and bright prospects for every young man, regardless of abilities or background. These Conference papers are a welcome contribution to the debate on reasons and measures we should all take to prevent suicide and alleviate the 'sorrows of young men.'

Iain Gray MSP
Deputy Minister for Community Care
The Scottish Executive

Preface

On 13 November 1999 the Centre for Theology and Public Issues in the University of Edinburgh brought together in conference well over a hundred people drawn from various specialisms and backgrounds, to examine together the disturbing phenomenon of the increasing risk of suicide among men between 15 and 45.

The fact of this increase not only in Scotland but throughout Europe is beyond debate; but what is debatable is the explanation. Alternative theories are put forward, but they are speculative and little researched. Changes in work, family, gender relations, culture, religion, media, health services – these and other factors are adduced as causes.

Through the meeting of a wide range of professionals to examine both the data and the theories, the conference sought to move beyond mere speculation, to gain deeper insight and to identify possible directions for policy, practice and research.

This volume incorporates the main contributions to the conference and an account of its deliberations. It is offered as an aid to the search for more effective ways of preventing suicide.

The views expressed are those of the contributors and are not to be taken as necessarily representative of the Centre.

The Centre is grateful for financial support for this conference from the Yapp Charitable Trusts, the Health Education Board for Scotland, the Scottish Development Centre for Mental Health Services and the Church of Scotland Board of Social Responsibility.

Centre for Theology and Public Issues
New College
The University of Edinburgh
Mound Place
Edinburgh
June 2000

List of Contributors

Professor Stephen Platt
Director of the Research Unit in Health and Behavioural Change, The University of Edinburgh.

Professor Jochen Clasen
Department of Applied Social Science, The University of Stirling

Professor Gill Jones
Department of Sociology and Anthropology, The University of Keele

The Most Reverend Richard Holloway
Primus of the Scottish Episcopal Church

Dr Cameron Stark
Consultant in Public Health Medicine, Highland Health Board

Dr Andrew Fraser
Deputy Chief Medical Officer, The Scottish Executive

Rev Dr Andrew Morton
Associate Director of the Centre for Theology and Public Issues, The University of Edinburgh

Stephen Platt

SUICIDE RISK AMONG YOUNG ADULTS IN SCOTLAND: EXAMINING THE EVIDENCE, EXPLAINING TRENDS AND REVIEWING OPTIONS FOR PREVENTION

Introduction

Suicidal behaviour among young people tends, quite understandably, to generate considerable societal disquiet and even panic. All governments attempt, within available resources, to minimise the loss of potential years of life represented by death among adolescents and young adults, but high levels of deliberate self-harm, particularly with fatal outcome, send out disturbing signals about the quality of life and prospects for the future, as experienced by younger generations. While mental health is recognised as a leading priority for the NHS in Scotland in the recently published White Paper on public health in Scotland (SODoH, 1999), suicide is not specifically identified as a target for action. Nevertheless, mental health practitioners, public health specialists, professional organisations (eg the British Medical Association) and the mass media have been voicing ever increasing concerns and urging action to tackle the rising tide of suicide among young Scottish men. This paper is intended to contribute to the continuing debate and search for practical and practicable solutions by examining the evidence about suicide trends, outlining and evaluating explanations for these trends, and reviewing the options for effective suicide prevention strategies. The epidemiological data presented here relate to Scotland over the past three decades, but it is hoped that the discussion on explanations and solutions will be equally pertinent to the rest of the UK where very similar trends in suicide have been noted.

Stephen Platt

EXAMINING THE EVIDENCE

International comparisons

In common with the rest of the UK, Scotland does not have an exceptionally high suicide rate by international standards. In a comparison with 20 other European countries Scotland was ranked 18th in respect of the adult (15+ years) male suicide rate and 17th in respect of the adult female suicide rate (Platt, 1988). (England and Wales was in 19th and 18th place, respectively.) However, an examination of *trends* in suicide across 22 countries (including Scotland) over the period 1974 to 1992 (Pritchard, 1996) reveals a different picture, complicated by the existence of marked variations by gender and age group. The patterning of trends in female suicide is very much in line with the findings of the cross-sectional comparison. The suicide rate among adult (15+ years) women in Scotland was 21st overall (with only England and Wales having a lower rate), and in all but one age group the Scottish rate was no higher than 16th. (The exception was the 25-34 age group for which Scotland had the fourth highest rate.) Trends among adult Scottish men were not so benign. In respect of the increase in the overall adult suicide rate, Scotland was placed fifth out of the 22 countries, with an increase of 55% compared to the median increase of 23%. Similarly high rankings were found for the 15-24 age group (fourth highest ranking, increase of 145% compared to the median increase of 29%), the 25-34 age group (fourth, increase of 103% compared to the median increase of 55%), the 35-44 age group (second, increase of 101% compared to the median increase of 5%) and the 55-64 age group (second, increase of 72% compared to the median decline of 13%). The decline in the male suicide rate among 45-54 and 65-74 year olds was around the international median and the decline in the 75+ age group was ranked 20th.

These international data suggest that, while Scotland does not have a high level of suicide relative to other countries, there have

2

nevertheless been worrying trends in suicide which require further investigation, particularly among young to mid-aged men and among females in their mid-20s to mid-30s. In the next section more detailed and up-to-date information about suicide in Scotland is presented.

Suicide in Scotland 1971-98 [1]

Time trends by gender

Gender-specific suicide rates (among all aged 15+ years) over the period under review are presented in graphical form in Figure 1. It is very difficult to discern any trend among females, with rates fluctuating narrowly between a low of 5.5 (in 1990) and a high of 9.6 (in 1975). However, there is some suggestion of a decline from 1979 to 1990, with a slight increase thereafter. Over the period 1971-3 to 1996-8 [2] the overall adult female suicide rate fell by 15.3% (from 8.5 to 7.2). (Actual suicide deaths fell from a mean of 174 per annum in 1971-3 to 157 per annum in 1996-8.) By contrast, the trend among males was

---

[1] Although it is now accepted good practice to include deaths given the ICD-9 codes E980-989 (excluding E988.8) ('injury undetermined whether accidentally or purposely inflicted') in the definition of suicide (Charlton *et al* 1992), only officially recorded suicide deaths (coded E950-959, 'suicide and self-inflicted injury') are considered here. All analyses have been repeated using the wider definition of suicide (ie incorporating 'undetermined' deaths) and reveal similar findings. Data referring to children aged under 15 years are excluded. Suicide is rarely given as an official cause of death in this age group. Where rates are presented, the denominator is per 100 000 population (by age group, gender or age group by gender)

[2] Three year averages are used in order to smooth out year on year fluctuations resulting from small Ns.

markedly (albeit not uninterruptedly) upwards, with each peak higher than the previous one. The overall adult male suicide rate rose by 76%, from 13.0 in 1971-3 to 22.9 in 1996-8. (The mean annual number of suicide deaths was 236 in 1971-3 and 456 in 1996-8.)

Age-specific suicide rates: changing pattern over time

Age-specific suicide rates in Scotland in 1971-3 and 1996-8 are presented in Figure 2 (males) and Figure 3 (females). In both genders in 1971-3 there was a tendency for rates to increase with age, peaking in the 65-74 year olds (males) and 55-64 year olds (females) and declining somewhat thereafter. This pattern should be contrasted with that found at the present time. Among males (figure 2) the peak rate is now found in the 25-34 age group, with the next highest rates in the 35-44 and 45-54 age groups. The increase in rates in the 65-74 and 75+ age groups (compared to the 55-64 age group) hints at a bimodal distribution. Among women there is no clear age-related pattern at all, with peaks in the 25-34, 45-54 and 65-74 age groups.

Age-specific trends over time

Age-specific trends in suicide rates, separately for males and females, are explored in Figure 4. Between 1971-3 and 1996-8 there were increases among men in all age groups except 55-74 years. Rates among 15-24 and 35-44 year olds more than doubled (+129% and +105%, respectively), while the rate among 25-34 year olds more than trebled (+245%). The mean annual total of suicide deaths in 1996-8 was 60 (up from 31 in 1971-3) among 15-24 year olds, 143 (up from 32) among 25-34 year olds and 97 (up from 38) among 35-44 year olds. The rate of increase was lower in the 45-54 and 75+ age groups (+42% and +16%, respectively).

Among women over the same period suicide rates fell in all age groups except 15-34 years. Among 15-24 year olds there was a

4

more than trebling (+239%) of the rate. Although this spectacular increase far exceeded that found for males in the same age group (+129%), it should be noted that the base in 1971-3 was very low: the rate was 1.8 and the mean annual total of suicide deaths was only seven; by 1996-8 the rate was 6.1 and the mean annual total of suicide deaths 19. The increase in the 25-34 age group was more modest (+55%); the mean annual total of suicide deaths rose from 19 in 1971-3 to 36 in 1996-8.

As a consequence of the differential gender trends, the excess of overall adult suicide among males compared to females widened considerably over the period. The overall male: female suicide ratio more than doubled, from 1.5 in 1971-3 to 3.2 in 1996-8. This increase in the male: female suicide ratio was found in all age groups except 15-24 year olds, the ratio falling from 4.3 in 1971-3 to 2.9 in 1996-8.

It is only possible to speculate about the possibility that these changes in the pattern of age-specific suicide are wholly or partly the result of a cohort effect. Data from England and Wales (Charlton *et al* 1992) certainly suggests that, for men, recent birth cohorts have higher mortality at the same age than earlier birth cohorts. Thus, when aged 15-19 years, the cohort born around 1971 had a higher suicide rate than the cohort born around 1966, which in turn had a higher suicide rate than the cohort born around 1956. The reverse trend (lower suicide rate with succeeding birth cohorts) was found for women aged 45 years and over. Charlton *et al* (1992) conclude that this constitutes evidence of a cohort effect on suicide among both men and women. "It is possible that suicide rates among young men may continue to rise as these cohorts grow older, while female suicide rates may continue to fall. The recent rise in suicide rates among the youngest women may, however, later extend into older age-groups" (p12).

Suicide as an important cause of death

Across the whole adult population suicide is an extremely rare cause of death. In 1971-3 only 0.8% of deaths (less than one in a hundred) among Scottish male adults resulted from suicide; by 1996-8 this proportion had doubled (to 1.6%) but still represented a modest contribution to overall male mortality. Among women the percentage of adult deaths coded as suicide was lower and fell slightly (from 0.6% to 0.5%) over the period under review.

However, these data mask the importance of suicide as an (ever more) important cause of death in younger adult age groups. Considering first the male population (Figure 5), suicide now accounts for 17.8% (up from 7.4% in 1971-3) of deaths in the 15-24 age group, 26.8% (8.3% in 1971-3) of deaths in the 25-34 age group, and 12.2% (4.4% in 1971-3) of deaths in the 35-44 age group.

A similar picture emerges when age-specific trends in suicide as a cause of death among women is examined (Figure 6). Suicide now constitutes 16.4% of deaths (up from 4.7%) in the 15-24 age group, 17.7% of deaths (up from 8.3%) in the 24-34 age group, and 5.9% of deaths (up from 4.3%) in the 35-44 age group.

Methods of suicide

In 1971-3 the most common method of suicide was self-poisoning (ICD-9 E950), accounting for 32% of male and 61% of female suicide deaths. Among males other preferred methods (accounting for over 10% of suicide deaths) included hanging (E953) (21%), drowning (E954) (13%) and domestic gas poisoning (E951) (10%). Among females hanging (15%) was the only other frequently used method. By 1996-8 the profile of methods used in suicide had changed. Among men hanging accounts for 44% of deaths (proportion up considerably since 1971-3), with self-poisoning contributing 22% (decline in proportion since 1971-3) and 'poisoning by other gases' (E952- mainly carbon monoxide poisoning by means of car exhaust fumes) 13% (considerable rise since 1971-3). Among women self-poisoning remains the main method of suicide (52%), but hanging is now widely used (24%) also. Following the distinction made by Platt *et al* (1988) between three different types of method ('active', comprising hanging, jumping (E957), firearms (E955) and cutting (E956); 'passive', comprising self-poisoning, poisoning by other gases and other unspecified methods(E958); and drowning (E954)), it can be shown that there has been an overall trend towards more active methods over the period under review. Among males, active methods were used in 34% of suicides in 1971-3 and 55% in 1996-8; among females the respective percentages were 13% and 31%.

Figures 7 and 8 show variations in major methods of suicide by age group among men and women, respectively. Age-related trends in poisoning (increasing use with age) and hanging and jumping (E957) (decreasing use with age) are evident for men. In the 15-24 age group active methods tend to be most used (67% of suicide deaths), and passive methods least used (29%); this difference in preferred type of method tends to decrease with increasing age (51% of 45+ year olds selecting active methods and 43% selecting passive methods). There are no clear age-related patterns in choice of specific suicide method among women.

RISK FACTORS FOR SUICIDE

There is a massive international literature on the epidemiology of suicide, in which groups at increased risk of suicide have been identified. In the absence of information relating specifically to

Scotland, I draw primarily upon data from England & Wales, Great Britain or the UK.

Socio-demographic factors

The influence of gender (excessive risk among males, increasing with time) and age group (changing pattern over time, with greatest risk for males now among 25-54 year olds and, among females, spread throughout the age range) has been examined above. Additional socio-demographic risk factors include marital status, social class, occupation and unemployment. Evidence of an aggregate-level association between divorce and suicide trends over time is overwhelming (eg Zimmerman, 1995). Individual-level data for England and Wales show that, among males aged 15-44 years over the period 1972-89, the widowed and divorced had the highest suicide rates, followed by the single and the married. "At given ages single men have suicide rates that are almost as high as those for divorced men. In general in each ten-year age-group, apart from the 15-24 year olds, single, widowed, and divorced men have suicide rates which are about three times greater than those of married men" (Charlton *et al.*, 1993, p36).

Two studies of variation in suicide by social class in Great Britain (Kreitman *et al.*, 1991, Drever *et al.*, 1997) report lower standardised mortality ratios (SMRs[3]) in the non-manual social classes (I, II, IIINM) and among semi-skilled workers (IIIM) and significantly elevated suicide SMRs in the semi- and unskilled manual classes (IV and V). Kreitman *et al.* (1991) confirmed the finding of higher SMRs for classes IV and V in England and Wales around 1981 for Scotland at about the same time and for all three countries around 1971. In a subsequent analysis Drever *et al.* (1997) found the same inverse relationship between social

---

[3] SMRs "are used to compare deaths in different segments of the population, taking into account differences in their composition....SMRs below 100 indicate lower mortality than expected. SMRs greater than 100 indicate higher than average mortality" (Drever and Bunting, 1997, p96).

class and suicide in England and Wales for the period 1991-3. One other important finding by Kreitman *et al.* (1991) was a significant interaction between age and social class. Figure 9 presents the relevant data (taken from Kreitman *et al.* 1991) in respect of Scottish males around 1981. Although the pattern is not entirely consistent (see, e.g., the high suicide rate in 45-54 year olds in social class 1), almost certainly due to the effects of small numbers and random fluctuations, the excess of suicide among those aged 25-54 in social class V (unskilled) is evident.

Analysis of variation in suicide risk by occupational group is reported in three publications relating to England and Wales (Charlton *et al.,* 1992, Kelly *et al.,* 1995, Kelly and Bunting, 1998). The statistic used in these studies is the proportional mortality ratio (PMR), which is the number of observed suicide deaths divided by the number of expected suicide deaths, expressed as a percentage[4]. During the 1980s and early 1990s medical and allied occupations and farming appeared to carry the highest suicide risk among males, while among females additional groups with elevated PMRs were nurses, professionals in education, health and welfare and those in personal service employment.

Kelly and Bunting (1998) draw attention to the discrepancy between the *PMR-based* findings, with high suicide risk occupations coming predominantly from social classes I and II

---

[4] "The expected deaths are computed by applying the proportion of total deaths due to suicide in the comparison ... population (... all men aged 20-64 or all women aged 20-59) to the total deaths in the occupation group of interest" (Kelly and Bunting, 1998). This statistic is used where the total number of individuals in an occupational group and their age distribution is not known, so that the SMR cannot be computed. It should be noted, however, that the PMR for suicide in a particular group can be misleading since it depends not only on the number of deaths from suicide in the group but also on the number of deaths from other causes. Thus an elevated suicide PMR may represent a true difference, but can also reflect a relative deficit of deaths from other causes.

(see above) and *SMR-based* findings, which show much lower suicide rates in the same social classes. They speculate that "the high PMRs found for doctors, vets and dentists reflect the fact that their overall mortality is low and therefore the proportion of deaths from suicide is high relative to other causes." Empirical support for this suggestion can be found in Charlton *et al.* (1992). Nevertheless, there is also evidence from other data and other countries that at least some of the occupational groups with high PMRs are generally at increased risk of suicide. Thus, a systematic review of suicide mortality in medical doctors (Lindeman *et al.*, 1996) estimates relative risks of between 1.1 and 3.4 in male doctors, and from 2.5 to 5.7 in female doctors, compared to the general population, and from 1.5 to 3.8 in males and from 3.7 to 4.5 in females compared to other professionals. Hawton and Vislisel (1999), reviewing the literature on suicide in nurses, note that findings from the majority of studies confirm a "substantially elevated" relative risk of suicide in female nurses. Finally, high rates of suicide in farmers have been reported in several, but not all, studies from North America, France and Australia (reviewed by Hawton *et al.*, 1998).

The relationship between unemployment and suicide has been investigated in considerable depth (see Platt (1984) and Platt and Hawton (2000) for reviews). The strongest evidence comes from individual-level longitudinal studies which report higher risk of suicide (whether measured by the odds ratio (OR), relative risk (RR) or SMRs) among the unemployed compared to the employed. The most rigorous analyses were those based on the England & Wales Longitudinal Study. Lewis and Sloggett (1998) calculated an OR of 2.6 for suicide over a 20 year follow-up period among those unemployed at baseline, after controlling for a range of socio-demographic variables. Their findings support the conclusion reached by Moser *et al.* (1984, 1986, 1987), based on a shorter follow-up period and controlling only for social class, that there is " direct effect of unemployment on mortality among those most directly affected by the experience."

Based on the findings collated in their review, Platt and Hawton (2000) estimate that, over the medium-long term, the risk of suicide (OR or RR) among the unemployed compared to the employed is between twofold and threefold.

Psychopathology

A further set of risk factors relates to individual psychopathology, covering mental illness and psychiatric status, history of deliberate self-harm and substance misuse. Psychiatric disturbance has been established as necessary, but not sufficient, for the occurrence of suicide, based on evidence from studies of suicide populations using psychological autopsy techniques (Hawton *et al.*, 1999). The most common diagnoses are affective disorder, schizophrenia and alcohol misuse (Roy, 1986). Conversely, between 10 and 15 per cent of people with schizophrenia and 15% of people with affective disorder will go on to commit suicide (Miles, 1977; Hawton, 1987). On the basis of their systematic review, Gunnell and Frankel (1994) conclude that current or former psychiatric patients experience an approximately tenfold risk of suicide, while Goldacre *et al.* (1993) estimate the magnitude of increased suicide risk for recently (within one month) discharged patients from general hospital at 130 and for the subsequent 11 months at 34.

A history of deliberate self harm increases suicide risk by an estimated magnitude of 10-30 (Gunnell and Frankel, 1994). Up to half of people who commit suicide have a history of deliberate self-harm, while about one per cent of people who deliberately harm themselves will go on to kill themselves in the first year, rising to a maximum of about 10% (Roy, 1986). "The relationship between alcohol and other drug misuse and suicide is well established" (Charlton *et al.*, 1993, p37). Similarly high (twenty fold) risks of suicide among 'alcoholics' and heroin users have been established. The elevated suicide risk among prisoners (Gunell and Frankel, 1994) is very likely linked to the high prevalence of psychopathology in this population (in addition, of course, to suicidogenic conditions within the prison environment and the impact of loss of liberty).

RISK CONDITIONS FOR SUICIDE

While this is an extensive list of high risk suicide groups and conditions, it is important to heed the warning that "many suicides do not belong to any defined high group" (Gunnell and Frankel, 1994, p1227). This important point has implications for the choice of strategies for preventing suicide. In addition to focusing on high-risk *groups*, it is equally necessary to consider a more radical population approach which targets broader risk *conditions*, thereby (potentially) reducing the size of the population at risk or the magnitude or quality of the risk factor itself (primary prevention). Established risk conditions for suicide include: (factual) reporting or (fictional) representation of suicidal behaviour in the print and broadcast media (Platt, 1994); availability of, and easy access to, lethal methods for suicide (Charlton *et al.*, 1993; Kelly and Bunting, 1998); labour market conditions (Platt and Hawton, 2000); and the state of the macro-economy, particularly the level of unemployment (Gunnell *et al.*, 1999; Platt, 1984; Platt and Hawton, 2000).

An additional risk condition, characterised as the "Easterlin effect" after the demographer who developed the hypothesis, has also been extensively debated. Easterlin (1973) suggests that economic and social fortunes stem from relative economic status, which is the comparison of income-earning possibilities to expected standard of living. Cohort size is the key determinant of both income potential (which depends on the size of the cohorts entering the labour market) and expected standard of living (which depends on the size of the cohorts of the previous generation). Easterlin (1980) claimed that an increase in the size of a birth cohort relative to the general or parental population produces increased competition for scarce resources, including education, employment and health care, resulting in relative deprivation for large cohorts and an increase in social disruption. From an early attempt to link shifting relative cohort size with fertility patterns, Easterlin went on to argue that this phenomenon also explained trends in marriage, divorce, education, female labour force participation, homicide and suicide. There is some empirical support for the existence of an Easterlin effect in respect of suicide among young adults, but there are also negative findings (see, e.g., Holinger, 1987; Leenaars and Lester, 1996; Freeman, 1998; Pampel, 1996). No relevant studies have yet been conducted on Scottish data.

EXPLAINING SUICIDE TRENDS AMONG YOUNG ADULTS

Before outlining the various explanations for the rising trend in suicide among young adults, it is necessary to point out the false assumptions that underlie some of the debate. In the first place, as we have seen, the increased trend in suicide is not confined to males. While it is true that the overall rate among women in Scotland fell somewhat over the period 1971-98, increases among those aged 15-34 years have been registered. The reasons for the increase in suicide in males and females aged 15-34 years may well differ, but it is possible that there are underlying factors which are common to both genders across the age group. Failure to notice the increase in suicide among young adult women may have resulted in an over-emphasis upon the influence of gender in accounting for trends over time. It has been shown that the gender gap in suicide actually narrowed among 15-24 year olds between 1971 and 1998. (Nevertheless, it of course remains the case that, even in this age group, suicide is predominantly a male behaviour.)

Second, the tendency to place excessive attention on males in the 15-24 year age group is misplaced, inasmuch as the greatest increase among males (and the highest overall suicide rate and numbers of suicide deaths) occurred among 25-34 year olds and a major increase was also noted in the 35-44 age group. What is required is a more encompassing theoretical framework which could account for all these complex changes in the socio-demographic risk profile of suicide.

The box lists various potential explanations for the rise in suicide among young adults in the UK and elsewhere. These are derived from several sources (see, especially, Berman and Jobes, 1995; Hawton, 1998) and from the author's own research experience in this area over two decades. Some explanations have been proposed in order to account for the rise in suicide among young males but could be equally well be applied to women. To state the argument in general terms, the noted suicide trends may arise as a result of an increase in the 'pool' of vulnerable individuals (or only males) in the relevant age groups, or an increase in the risk of suicide within a vulnerable 'pool' of stable size, or both processes.

A specific example, *psychopathology: affective disorder* (the first item in the box), might be helpful here. On the one hand, the increase in suicide among young adults aged 15-34 years may have resulted from an increase in the number of individuals in this age group who suffer from affective disorder and who are therefore vulnerable to suicidal impulses and behaviour. Even if the rate of suicide among those with affective disorders remains the same, the actual suicide rate in the age group will rise (other things being equal) because the population at risk has grown larger. On the other hand, there may have been no increase in the number of people with affective disorder but the suicide risk associated with this psychiatric condition may have increased (eg as a result of concomitant changes in the symptom profile or greater prevalence of co-morbidity, especially conditions which also produce an elevated suicide risk). Consequently, again other things being equal, the suicide rate in the age group will increase. Of course both processes may be occurring simultaneously: an increased 'pool' of vulnerable individuals and an increased risk of suicide among the vulnerable. This example would work equally well for several other explanations listed in the box, including physical/sexual abuse (eg a larger group of young adults who have suffered such abuse, a greater suicide risk among those who have been abused), socio-demographic change (eg more unmarried, greater suicide risk among the unmarried), labour market conditions (eg more unemployed or lacking job security, greater suicide risk among the unemployed/insecure), social exclusion, human capital and social capital.

An exception to these explanations which are not (necessarily or intrinsically) gender-specific can be found under the *culture and communication* heading (box). The socialisation theory argues that there are gender differences in culturally acceptable self-destructive behaviours, with suicide being viewed as a masculine behaviour and attempted suicide as a feminine behaviour. "Men and women will tend to adopt the self-destructive behaviours that are congruent with the gender scripts of their cultures" (Canetto and Sakinofsky, 1998: 17). It has been argued that suicide data from the USA and Canada support the conclusion that the gender gap in suicide is more prominent in communities where different suicidal behaviours are expected of males and females. Whether or not the socialisation theory is applicable to Scottish culture, and whether or not the conflicting Scottish evidence (males and females in the 15-34 age group exhibiting similar secular trends in suicide but suicide remaining an overwhelmingly male behaviour) supports the socialisation theory, are questions open to considerable debate.

The final set of explanations outlined in the box concerns the quality of the health service response. If this factor is to account for the rise in the suicide rate among young adults, it logically follows that there must have been some deterioration over the past three decades. In respect of primary care, general practitioners would have had to become less proficient at recognising suicidal risk and detecting and treating the psychopathology which predisposes to suicide. Hospital-based services must have failed to stabilise suicidal behaviour among psychiatric patients under their care. I am unaware of any published Scottish data which can refute or confirm these hypotheses.

Box   Potential explanations for the rise in suicide among young adults

Psychopathology

• affective disorder

• substance abuse/misuse (alcohol and drugs)

• depression

• conduct disorder

Physical/sexual abuse

Availability of means and ease of access

• firearms

• carbon monoxide poisoning (car exhaust fumes)

Socio-demographic change

• marital breakdown/divorce

• later marriage

• shifting relative cohort size

[*continued over...*]

Culture and communication

- cultural script model/socialisation
- gendered role expectations
- media reporting
- societal attitudes

Labour market conditions

- unemployment
- rise of non-standard workforms/job insecurity

Social exclusion

- imprisonment
- homelessness
- poverty/deprivation

Human capital

- lacking/poor education
- lacking/poor lifeskills
- lacking/poor technical skills
- lacking/poor interpersonal skills

Social capital

- inadequate social support
- lack of social cohesion
- impoverished social networks and inter-connectedness

[*continued over...*]

Quality of health service response

- deterioration in response at primary care level
- deterioration in response at secondary care level

OPTIONS FOR EFFECTIVE SUICIDE PREVENTION STRATEGIES AMONG YOUNG ADULTS

In line with the distinction made above, strategies for preventing suicide can be divided into two types: high risk groups and high risk conditions (population-based). Lewis *et al.* (1997) suggest targeting prevention efforts at three specific high risk groups: those recently discharged from psychiatric hospital, those referred to general hospital following an episode of non-fatal deliberate self-harm, and high-risk occupational groups, such as doctors and farmers. With respect to population-based strategies, Lewis *et al.* (1997) identify two potential approaches: reducing the availability or toxicity of commonly available methods for committing suicide (especially analgesics, anti-depressants and car exhaust gases); and public health measures, such as a reduction in the level of unemployment. Other public health measures that have been proposed in the literature as potentially valuable suicide prevention strategies include: improved safety measures at suicide 'hotspots'; greater control over (factual) reporting and (fictional) portrayal of suicide in the mass media; enhanced availability of professional counselling and support; and suicide prevention programmes in secondary and tertiary educational institutions.

In their extensive systematic review of the likely contribution of all possible strategies for the prevention of suicide, Gunnell and Frankel (1994) demonstrate the enormity of the task. In many cases the quality of the evidence about any effect on suicide incidence is uncertain or weak, or else the estimated reduction in suicide is small. Their conclusions relate to whole populations, and are based on data gathered from a variety of countries over a period of time. The level of uncertainty is even greater if any attempt is made to identify strategic approaches which will reduce suicide among young adults in Scotland at the start of the 21st century (and greater still if we restrict our attention to males only). Faced with the adverse suicide trends outlined in this paper, we find ourselves in the uncomfortable position of being unable to produce an evidence-based blueprint for preventive action. This is not a situation which can be permitted to continue. A concerted and co-ordinated response by practitioners, policy makers and researchers is overdue.

REFERENCES

Berman AL and Jobes DA (1995) Suicide prevention in adolescents (age 12-18). *Suicide and Life-Threatening Behavior* **25**: 143-154.

Canetto SS and Sakinofsky I (1998) The gender paradox in suicide. *Suicide and Life-Threatening Behavior* **28**: 1-23.

Charlton J, Kelly S, Dunnell K, Evans B and Jenkins R (1992) Suicide deaths in England and Wales. *Population Trends* **69**: 2-8.

Charlton J, Kelly S, Dunnell K, Evans B and Jenkins R (1993) Suicide deaths in England and Wales: trends in factors associated with suicide deaths. *Population Trends* **71**: 34-42.

Drever F and Bunting J (1997) Patterns and trends in male mortality. In: F Drever and M. Whitehead (eds.) *Health Inequalities*. London: The Stationery Office.

Drever F, Bunting J and Harding D (1997) Male mortality from major causes of death. In: F Drever and M. Whitehead (eds.) *Health Inequalities*. London: The Stationery Office.

Easterlin RA (1973) Relative economic status and the American fertility swing. In: EB Sheldon (ed.) *Family Economic Behavior.* Philadelphia: Lipincott.

Easterlin RA (1980) *Birth and Fortune.* New York: Basic Books.

Freeman DG (1998) Determinants of youth suicide: the Easterlin-Holinger cohort hypothesis re-examined. *American Journal of Economics and Sociology* **57**: 183-199.

Goldacre M, Seagrott V, Hawton K (1993) Suicide after discharge from psychiatric in-patient care. *Lancet* **342**: 283-286.

Gunnell D and Frankel S (1994) Prevention of suicide: aspirations and evidence. *BMJ* **308**: 1227-1233.

Gunnell D, Lopatatzidis A, Dorling D, Wehner H, Southall H and Frankel S (1999) Suicide and unemployment in young people. Analysis of trends in England and Wales, 1921-1995. *British Journal of Psychiatry* **175**: 263-270.

Hawton K (1987) Assessment of suicide risk. *British Journal of Psychiatry* **150**: 145-153.

Hawton K (1998) Why has suicide increased in young males? *Crisis* **19**: 119-124.

Hawton K., Simkin S, Malmberg A, Fagg J and Harriss L (1998) *Suicide and Stress in Farmers.* London: The Stationery Office

Hawton K, Houston K and Shepperd R (1999) Suicide in young people. Study of 174 cases, aged under 25 years, based on coroners' and medical records. *British Journal of Psychiatry* **175**: 271-276.

Hawton K. and Vislisel L (1999) Suicide in nurses. *Suicide and Life-Threatening Behavior* **29**: 86-95.

Holinger PC (1987) *Violent Deaths in the United States.* New York: Guildford.

Kelly S, Charlton J and Jenkins R (1995) Suicide deaths in England and Wales, 1982-92: the contribution of occupation and geography. *Population Trends* **80**: 16-25.

Kelly S and Bunting J (1998) Trends in suicide in England and Wales, 1982-96. *Population Trends* **92**: 29-41.

Kreitman N, Carstairs V and Duffy, J (1991) Association of age and social class with suicide among men in Great Britain. *Journal of Epidemiology and Community Health,* **45**: 195-202.

Leenaars AA and Lester D (1996) Testing the cohort size hypothesis of suicide and homicide rates in Canada and the United States. *Archives of Suicide Research* **2**: 43-54.

Lewis G, Hawton K and Jones P (1997) Strategies for preventing suicide. *British Journal of Psychiatry* **171**: 351-354.

Lewis G and Sloggett A (1998) Suicide, deprivation, and unemployment: record linkage study. *BMJ* **317**: 1283-1286.

Lindeman S, Laara E, Hakko H and Lonnqvist J (1996) A systematic review on gender-specific suicide mortality in medical doctors. *British Journal of Psychiatry* **168**: 274-279.

Miles J (1977) Conditions predisposing to suicide: a review. *Journal of Nervous and Mental Disease* **164**: 231-246.

Moser KA, Fox AJ and Jones DR (1984) Unemployment and mortality in the OPCS longitudinal study. *Lancet* **ii**: 1324-1329.

Moser KA, Fox AJ, Jones DR and Goldblatt PO (1986) Unemployment and mortality: further evidence from the OPCS longitudinal study 1971-81. *Lancet* **i**: 365-367.

Moser KA, Goldblatt PO, Fox AJ and Jones DR (1987) Unemployment and mortality: comparison of the 1971 and 1981 longitudinal study census samples. *BMJ* **294**: 86-90.

Pampel FC (1996) Cohort size and age-specific suicide rates: a contingent relationship. *Demography* **33**: 341-355.

Platt S (1984) Unemployment and suicidal behaviour: a review of the literature. *Social Science and Medicine* **19**: 93-115.

Platt S (1988) Suicide trends in 24 European countries. In: H-J Moller, A Schmidtke and R Welz (eds.) *Current Issues in Suicidology*. Berlin: Springer-Verlag.

Platt S (1994) The media response. In: R Jenkins, S Griffiths, I Wylie, K Hawton, G Morgan and A Tylee (eds.) *The Prevention of Suicide*. London: HMSO.

Platt S and Hawton K (2000) Suicidal behaviour and the labour market. In: K Hawton and K van Heeringen (eds.) *International Handbook of Suicide and Attempted Suicide*. Chichester: John Wiley and Son.

Pritchard C (1996) New patterns of suicide by age and gender in the United Kingdom and the Western world 1974-1992; an indicator of social change? *Social Psychiatry and Psychiatric Epidemiology* **31**: 227-234.

Roy A (ed.) (1986) *Suicide.* Baltimore, MD: Williams and Wilkins.

Scottish Office Department of Health (SODoH) (1999) *Towards a Healthier Scotland.* Edinburgh: The Stationery Office.

Zimmerman SL (1995) Psychache in context. States' spending for public welfare and their suicide rates. Journal of Nervous and Mental Disease 183: 425-434.

Figure 1 Suicide rates (per 100,000 aged 15+ years), by gender, Scotland, 1971-98

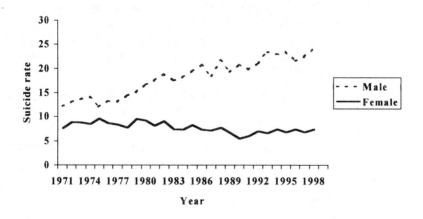

Figure 2 Suicide rates by age group, males, Scotland, 1971-3 and 1996-8

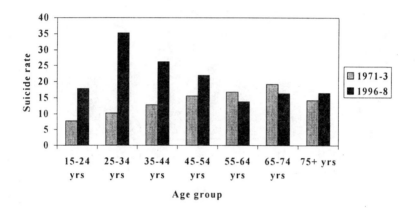

Figure 3 Suicide rates by age group, females, Scotland, 1971-3 and 1996-8

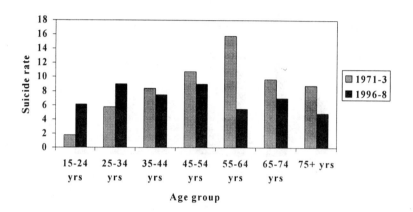

Figure 4 Percent change in suicide rate, by age group and gender, Scotland, 1971-3 to 1996-8

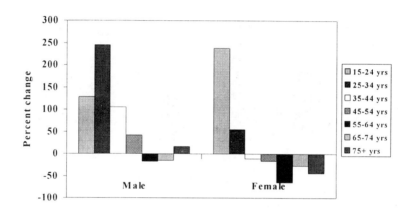

Figure 5 Suicide as proportion of all deaths, males, by age group, Scotland, 1971-73 and 1996-98

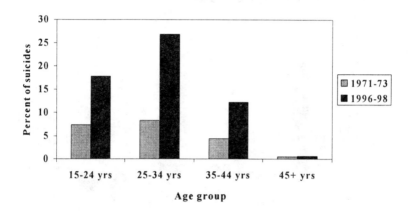

Figure 6 Suicide as proportion of all deaths, females, by age group, Scotland, 1971-73 and 1996-98

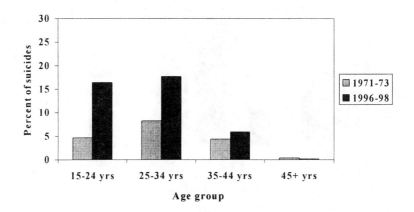

Figure 7 Suicide methods, males, by age group, Scotland, 1996-8

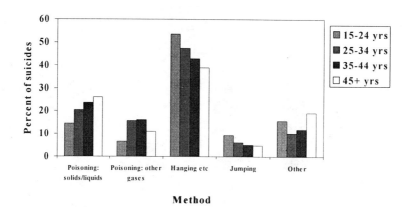

Figure 8 Suicide methods, females,by age group, Scotland, 1996-8

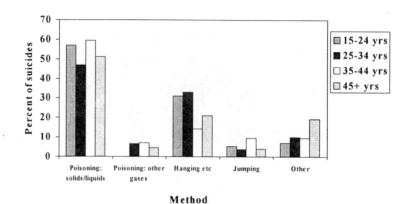

Figure 9 Male suicide mortality ratios, Scotland, 1979-83, by age group and social class

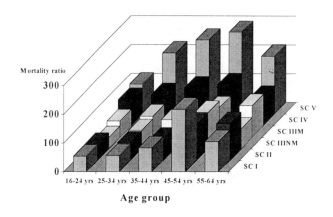

Age group

Jochen Clasen

LABOUR MARKET CHANGE AND LABOUR MARKET POLICY

Introduction

Elsewhere in this volume Stephen Platt (see pages 1 - 30) shows that Scottish and British suicide rates are not particularly high by international standards. However, the increase in suicide rates over the past 30 years has been more pronounced than in many other countries, and this applies to men under the age of 45 in particular. A little less than 30 years ago, unemployment levels also rose steeply and remained at very high levels by international standards throughout the 1980s and early 1990s. This suggests that there might be a connection between unemployment and suicide. Platt also refers to the extensive literature on this relationship and to the evidence, supported by his own research, that over the medium and long term the risk of suicide is considerably higher amongst the unemployed than for those in employment. Consequently, policies which facilitate labour market integration and high levels of employment could be considered as diminishing one of the risk factors for suicide by reducing the size of the population at risk.

The above seems ample justification for assessing the pattern and incidence of employment and unemployment in the UK, with particular reference to the labour market participation of young men over time and in international perspective. The second part of this article addresses this. In the first part, some more preliminary remarks about the relationship between unemployment and suicide are made. Finally, the article reflects briefly on current labour market policies aimed at increasing labour market integration.

Connecting Unemployment and Suicide

Unemployment affects not only living standards but also social integration. In addition, there is sufficient evidence that joblessness is associated with ill health and with lower levels of psychological well-being (Gallie and Russell, 1998). Studies show that psychological ill-health is more common among young than old unemployed people, among long-term rather than short-term unemployed and among men rather than women.

However, while unemployment seems to have an adverse effect on mental well-being, the reverse is equally plausible. In other words, for people with mental health problems access to the labour market might be more difficult and redundancy more likely. What is more, unemployment is associated with other factors such as poor housing, alcohol problems or poverty. Thus, rather than unemployment per se, it might be these 'confounding variables' (Smith, 1987) which are the more relevant factors influencing the risk of suicide. However, there appears to be some evidence that unemployment is not merely correlated with mental well-being but that the former has an adverse impact on the latter. According to Moser and Paul (1999), who examined 51 independent studies on the issue, the transition from unemployment to employment was found to have a significant positive effect, while a transition from school or employment into unemployment is coupled with an adverse impact on psychological well-being.

A recent survey of 50 long-term unemployed people under the age of 25 in West and East Germany confirms this (Kieselbach *et al.*, 1999). According to a combination of criteria which indicate different degrees and dimensions of social exclusion (economic, institutional, social isolation, cultural, geographical), three groups could be distinguished: those with no risk of social exclusion (n=10), those with a small risk of social exclusion (n=16), and those with a high risk of social exclusion (n=24). The group with only a small risk of social exclusion consisted mainly of people who were without a job but were not affected by other factors, such as social isolation or financial deprivation. By contrast, members of the group with a high risk of social exclusion were much more likely to have few or no qualifications, to be in a financial situation which was markedly worse than in the other groups, to be able to draw on only limited social and family support and to be without institutional help in finding a way back into employment. More than the other groups, young people in this group suffered from problems such as sleeplessness, worries about the future, frustration and despair, generally low psychological well-being and financial stress. What is more, almost half of the members of this group had either tried to commit suicide or had thought about it. In about half of those cases, unemployment was mentioned as the main reason. By comparison, suicidal tendencies associated with unemployment were not found in either of the two other groups.

The above example is based on cross-sectional and individual data. At an aggregate and longitudinal level too there is a clear association between unemployment and suicide, as Gunnell *et al.* (1999) have found for England and Wales between the 1920s and the mid 1990s. Generally, when unemployment started to rise in the early 1970s, suicide rates for men aged between 25 and 44 increased gradually but markedly. However, in the short term there seems to be a much less pronounced correlation between unemployment and suicide rates, as is shown in the decline of unemployment in the second half of the 1980s which is not matched by a similar reduction of suicide rates. In fact, Gunnell's recent data indicate a negative correlation between unemployment and suicide, particularly for the under 25 year-old age group.

This suggests at least two things. Firstly, as indicated above, unemployment is only one factor amongst others which increases the risk of suicide. Its impact seems to vary between different age groups. However, in many cases unemployment is at least an intermediary factor where it leads to poverty, relationship breakdown, stress or other adverse individual and social consequences. Secondly, unemployment is only one aspect of an economic recession. Less visible are consequences which might affect people who are still in employment. For example, the experience of an economic downturn might lead to higher levels of job insecurity generally and to a forced acceptance of different working patterns, such as short-time work or temporary employment. The following sections investigate both unemployment and employment patterns with respect to the position of young men.

Patterns of Unemployment

After the two oil price shocks and economic recessions in the mid 1970s and early 1980s the UK has ranked amongst the countries with the worst unemployment records in Western Europe, that is with unemployment rates of about 12 per cent or more. Irrespective of statistical definitions, this began to change in 1993 when unemployment started to fall gradually but steadily. Today, the UK can be considered as one of the four 'success' countries in Europe, along with Denmark, the Netherlands and Ireland (see Table 1). While other countries (Austria and Luxembourg, in particular) have lower unemployment, it is these four countries which have witnessed significant reductions of unemployment during the last decade. By contrast, the larger economies of Italy, Germany and France are now faced with the highest unemployment rates in Western Europe (Table 1).

Table 1: Total unemployment rates, selected countries, 1995-1999

Year	1995	1996	1997	1998	1999*
UK %	8.7	8.2	7.0	6.3	6.3
Denmark %	7.2	6.8	5.6	5.1	4.8
Netherlands %	6.9	6.3	5.2	4.0	3.6
Ireland %	12.3	11.6	9.8	7.8	7.0
Germany %	8.2	8.9	9.9	9.4	9.0
France %	11.7	12.4	12.3	11.7	11.4
Italy %	11.9	12.0	12.1	12.2	12.1
EU %	10.7	10.8	10.6	10.0	9.6
USA %	5.6	5.4	4.9	4.5	4.4

* February 1999; Italy: January 1999. *Source: Eurostat (1999).*

Two important aspects which Table 1 does not reveal are geographical patterns of unemployment and the incidence of workless households in the UK. A recent study (Turok and Edge, 1999) found that big cities in the north of England and in Scotland have not benefited from the increase in employment. While overall employment grew by 1.7 million jobs between 1981 and 1996, Britain's 20 major cities have lost 500,000 jobs. This decline, largely attributable to the contracting manufacturing base, has affected men in particular. The same study found that commuting to jobs elsewhere has not been a viable option for many people and that both registered and hidden unemployment is very high in these urban areas.

Second, rather than counting unemployment by adding the number of individuals, one could calculate the number of households without anybody in paid employment. Gregg and Wadsworth (1998) show that in many European countries a polarisation has developed since the early 1980s between work-rich two-earner and workless (no earner) households. In almost all EU countries the number of both types of households has increased, while the share of mixed households has been declining. Today, in over 60 per cent of all households in the UK all adults are in work. By contrast, almost 20 per cent of all households (with adults of working age) do not contain anybody in paid employment. Recent employment growth has not, therefore, benefited all households. Instead, 'jobs have been disproportionately taken by households where a working adult was already present' (Gregg and Wadsworth, 1998: 34). The workless household rate in the UK is high but not unusual in international comparison. Nevertheless, it is a cause for concern, given the better than average employment performance compared with other European countries.

Gender differences

When compared with other countries, the UK is unusual in that male unemployment is higher than female unemployment (see Table 2). Reasons for this have to do with the decline of predominantly male types of employment, such as manufacturing, and the growth of, predominantly, female types of employment in services. While this is a common trend across countries, it is particularly pronounced in the UK. In addition, what is often referred to as irregular types of employment (such as part-time and temporary work) have been growing and have been taken up more by women than by men. Other factors include cross-national differences in labour law (e.g. regarding employment protection and early retirement options) and social security arrangements (e.g. means-tested benefits are more frequently claimed by men and are a more relevant source of income maintenance in the UK than in most other

European welfare states).

Table 2: Male and female unemployment rates (percent), selected countries, 1995-1998

Year		1995	1996	1997	1998
UK	M	10.1	9.5	7.9	7.0
	F	7.0	6.5	6.0	5.5
Netherlands	M	6.9	6.3	5.2	4.0
	F	8.6	8.1	7.0	5.2
Denmark	M	5.9	5.5	4.6	3.9
	F	8.9	8.3	6.8	6.5
Germany	M	7.1	8.2	9.3	8.9
	F	9.6	9.8	10.7	10.2
France	M	9.8	10.6	10.6	9.9
	F	14.0	14.5	14.4	13.8

M: male; F: female *Source: Eurostat (1999)*

Youth unemployment

As with unemployment generally, youth unemployment, that is the rate of unemployment amongst those who are younger than 25 years of age, has declined (see Table 3). The reasons include improved labour market conditions generally and a stronger focus on labour market policies on younger people who, while on training and other programmes, are not counted as unemployed.

Table 3: Total unemployment rates (percent)and unemployment rates (percent) of persons under 25 years, selected countries, 1995-1998

Year	%	1995	1996	1997	1998
U K	Total	8.7	8.2	7.0	6.3
	Under 25	15.9	15.5	14.2	13.6
Netherlands	Total	5.7	5.0	3.9	3.0
	Under 25	12.0	11.7	9.6	7.8
Denmark	Total	7.2	6.8	5.6	5.1
	Under 25	10.6	10.6	8.4	7.4
Germany	Total	8.2	8.9	9.9	9.4
	Under 25	8.8	10.0	10.8	9.8
France	Total	11.7	12.4	12.3	11.7
	Under 25	27.5	29.2	29.1	26.6

Source: Eurostat(1999)

What the rates in Table 3 do not show is the increased participation of younger people in education and thus a lower rate of participation in employment and changing age composition of unemployment across the EU. In other words, there are now considerably fewer under 25 year olds and more 25 to 49 year olds in unemployment than in the mid 1980s (European Commission, 1998: 18). The 16 to 24-year-old group represented 38 per cent of all unemployed in 1984. This share dropped to 30 per cent in 1993 (*Labour Market Trends*, May 1998). By contrast, the percentage of all unemployed aged 25 to 39 years rose from 32 per cent to 37 per cent.

Nevertheless, young people are still disproportionately affected by unemployment. The ratio of youth to standard unemployment has been fairly stable at about 2:1 in the UK throughout this decade. This is much higher than in some countries, and particularly Germany, but overall represents a middle position within the EU.

There are significant differences in the prevalence of unemployment between young men and young women. In most EU countries, young women are more affected by unemployment than young men (see Table 4). The exceptions are Germany, Ireland and Sweden where men have a marginally higher risk of unemployment than women, and the UK where young men are clearly more affected than young women. The unemployment rate of young men is two and a half times the average unemployment rate.

Unemployment could be further analysed by a number of other criteria, such as level of skill, which would show that the ratio of unemployment among unskilled workers to the standard unemployment in the UK is high within European context. The average length of unemployment spells would be another relevant indicator for the degree of labour market exclusion. However, the latter tends to vary considerably over time with long-term unemployment declining, after some time lag, when overall unemployment decreases. Measurements are therefore highly sensitive to the point in the business cycle. For example, in 1997 two and a half per cent of the labour force in the UK had been out of a job for more than one year. Ten years earlier the respective share was 5 per cent (European Commission, 1998).

Table 4: Unemployment rates (percent) of men and women under 25 years, selected countries, 1995-1998

Year		1995	1996	1997	1998
UK	M	18.0	18.0	15.9	15.2
	F	13.3	12.5	12.2	11.7
Netherlands	M	11.3	11.1	8.3	7.6
	F	12.7	12.3	10.9	8.1
Denmark	M	8.5	8.8	7.0	6.8
	F	12.9	12.6	10.1	8.0
Germany	M	8.9	10.6	11.7	10.6
	F	8.7	9.2	9.8	9.0
France	M	23.9	26.3	26.6	24.2
	F	31.2	32.2	31.8	29.2

Source: Eurostat (1999)

The incidence of unemployment among young men

The tables above indicate levels of unemployment at a particular point in time and do not reveal anything about the distribution of unemployment. Analysing the incidence of unemployment in the UK based on benefit claimants and panel data, Teasdale (1998) found that 53 per cent of all employees in the 18-59 age group had experienced a spell of unemployment in the 14 years prior to 1996. The incidence of unemployment for men aged 30-39 was the highest (71 per cent). Within a shorter period (1992 to 1996), 29 per cent of working population over 18 (10 million people) had experienced a spell of unemployment. However, half of all claimants had made more than one claim in the last 12 months. This proportion had changed only little over time.

The likelihood of becoming unemployed is significantly higher for men than for women, and it is much higher for younger than older men. Based on unemployment claimant figures, more than 60 per cent of men in their early twenties had experienced a spell of unemployment between 1991 and 1996, and more than half of those were under the age of 30 (Teasdale 1998). However, while young men are more likely to experience a spell of unemployment than young women, young unemployed or economically inactive males have on average a stronger labour market attachment than older men or women (particularly those without dependent children). This applies to the age group 25 to 34 in particular. In the summer of 1998, about a third of all unemployed men in this age group had left their job less than 12 months before, compared with a fifth of men between 35 and 49 (*Labour Market Trends*, February 1999).

Most spells of unemployment are relatively short, with more than half ending within three months. During the period between 1992 and 1996, nearly a third of all unemployed left the register within six months and did not claim again. However, half of those who left the unemployment record returned to it within a year. Although the gap has narrowed between the mid 1980s and the mid 1990s, men have still a higher probability than women of returning to the ranks of the unemployed, and young people under the age of 25 are more likely to become unemployed again than those who are older.

Thus, while leaving unemployment is easier for younger than for older men, returning to unemployment is much more likely. What is more, Teasdale (1998) estimated that one in eight (claimant) unemployed had had more than three spells of unemployment during the five year period prior to 1996. Almost half of those were under 25 at the time of their first spell of unemployment. Earlier comparable panel data are not available but individual studies suggest that there has been an increase in the incidence of repeated spells of unemployment since the 1980s.

Patterns of employment

A focus on unemployment as a measurement of labour market change can be somewhat misleading since it does not indicate changes in patterns of labour market participation over time. Across the EU, the participation rate of those 15-64 remained fairly stable in the 1990s, but rose considerably in some countries and particularly in the Netherlands and Ireland. The number of men in the labour force has changed little over the past five years or so, with an increase in population being offset by a decline in participation (e.g. due to education or early retirement). By contrast, the number of women in employment rose steadily.

Part-time work, temporary jobs and self-employment

Part-time employment across the EU rose steadily from the early 1980s and accelerated during the 1990s, while the number of full-time jobs declined. Thus, although the economic recovery in many countries led to more people finding jobs from the early 1990s, this was marked with a shift from full-time to part-time employment. Between 1994 and 1997, for example, the number of part-time jobs went up by over 10 per cent across the EU. This shift affected both men and women. Nevertheless, the extent of part-time work is still very different across countries and less pronounced for men as opposed to women (see European Commission, 1998: 24). After the Netherlands, the UK has the second highest female part-time employment rate in the EU (with about 45 per cent of all women working on a part-time basis) and one of the highest male part-time rates. While the latter is still relatively low (about 9 per cent), the share of previously unemployed men entering part-time employment has been growing steadily over the 1990s, reaching 20 per cent in 1997 (European Commission, 1998: 25).

Other forms of non-standard employment include temporary work and self-employment. The share of people with fixed-term contracts has grown steadily across the EU but is still relatively low (11 per cent for men and 13 per cent for women in 1997). Perhaps surprisingly, while there has been an increase also in the UK during the 1990s, by 1997 temporary contracts for both British men and women were well below the EU average (about 6 per cent and 8 per cent, respectively). As for part-time jobs, fixed-term contracts are becoming increasingly important for previously unemployed men and women, but less so in the UK than in most other EU countries. The proportion of previously unemployed men entering temporary types of work is slightly higher than the equivalent proportion of women.

Finally, self-employment has grown since the mid 1980s. About 13 per cent of those employed in industry and services in the EU were self-employed, with about 40 per cent of these employing other people. The UK's profile is fairly close to the EU average, but self-employment is more pronounced than in other large economies of Germany, France or labour market success countries Denmark and the Netherlands.

Despite their growth, the focus on non-standard forms of employment is somewhat misleading. Over the previous year, the increase in the number of full-time employees in the UK was still two and a half times the number of the increase in part-time employees. What is more, while almost half of all women work part-time, three quarters of the increase in full-time jobs went to women - and the growth in female full-time jobs was twice as high as the increase in female part-time jobs (*Labour Market Trends*, May 1999).

Labour Market Insecurity

While the participation in the labour market might have a positive effect on individual well-being, having a job might also give rise to anxieties, not least of losing a job. A recent OECD publication (OECD, 1997) assessed studies on job insecurity across countries. While data are not always directly comparable, the International Social Survey Programme (ISSP) indicates a high level of employment insecurity in the UK. Indeed, a composite indicator suggests that between 1993 and 1996 job insecurity in the UK increased to a level which was higher than in any other in European country, with similar levels recorded only in France. Other survey data confirm a steep increase in perceived job insecurity in 1992 in the UK and high levels since then, even though unemployment declined during the same period (Spencer 1996).

Are there marked differences across social groups? The same OECD publication (OECD, 1997) reviewed data from the British Household Panel Survey which show that the percentage of employees not completely satisfied with their job security rose in the early 1990s and has remained fairly stable since then (between 75 and 80 per cent). Men are consistently less satisfied about their jobs than women, although the gap is not marked (about five percentage points in 1995). As to age groups, it is the middle aged (25-44) who are less happy in their jobs than their younger and older colleagues; once again the differences are consistent over time, but not particularly large (five percentage points).

In sum, the UK has high levels of job insecurity, with men between 25 and 44 somewhat more affected than other groups. If this cannot be explained with reference to changes in unemployment, other possible reasons might be short job tenures and frequent change of jobs. In the UK, the average job tenure is 8.3 years, with 18 per cent of tenures lasting less than one year. Perhaps surprisingly, given the increase in job insecurity and labour market participation, these figures have changed little between the mid 1980s and the mid 1990s (OECD, 1997: 14). In comparison with other European countries, job tenure is very short in the UK, and more similar to that in the USA, Canada and Australia. This is probably influenced by weaker employment protection measures and labour law regulations in the UK compared with the rest of Europe, apart from Denmark.

Overall, the short average job tenure in the UK corresponds with the relatively high level of job insecurity. Employees in other

European countries with high job turnover rates and short average tenures, such as Denmark, seem much less worried about job security. Even in Spain, where more than a fifth of the workforce changes jobs within six months, employees feel less insecure in their jobs than in the UK.

Labour Market Policies

Since the end of the 1980s, a main thrust of labour market policies in the UK has been to make conditionality of benefits more explicit, tightening controls, prescribing job seeking behaviour and stiffening sanctions for non-compliance (Finn 1997). The Labour government in 1997 intensified the emphasis on behavioural aspects, which reflects a more general attempt to redefine rights and responsibilities within the British welfare state (Plant 1998). In essence this involves the propagation of a new 'contract' between citizens and the state, with the latter offering different types of assistance for labour market integration and the former being obliged to accept this assistance (DSS, 1998). Most prominent in terms of mandatory labour market participation programmes has been the 'New Deal' for young unemployed people (Deacon, 1997; Warton *et al.*, 1998; Finn 1999). In brief, for claimants under the age of 25 individual 'activity plans' are drawn up with the Employment Service, which require the transition from benefit receipt to a subsidised job in the private or public sector or full time education. The focus on labour market integration is also evident in other New Deal programmes (e.g. for lone parents) and a range of other social security and tax policies.

The introduction of welfare to work policies, and the New Deal in particular, marks a watershed in British labour market policy. Previous conservative governments were reluctant to increase expenditure on labour market policies for fiscal and ideological reasons. By contrast, the Labour administration has channelled earmarked public funds into new programmes which have a significantly higher degree of coherence than the patchwork of earlier schemes. New Labour also introduced an element of obligation as an explicit *quid pro quo* for this investment in better labour market integration programmes, with a focus on young and long-term unemployed people.

Early results show that the New Deal has made a difference in terms of young people leaving claimant unemployment for jobs, education, training and employment programmes. Teasdale (1998) shows that those who left claimant unemployment in June 1995 for government-supported training returned to unemployment within a year. Comparisons are perhaps a little premature but there are clear indications that the New Deal has improved the job entry levels of young unemployed people, and that this has not occurred at the expense of job entry rates for older long-term or shorter-term unemployed people (Bivand, 1999a). On the other hand, the introduction of the New Deal has not reduced the share of those who leave the claimant count for unknown destinations. Also, while almost half of all young people who had left the New Deal by July 1999 had done so for unsubsidised jobs, for 40 per cent of them those jobs lasted less than 13 weeks. As for the New Deal for older long-term unemployed people, just 16 per cent of those who left the programme did so for an unsubsidised job, compared with well over half who returned to Job Seekers Allowance or other benefits (Bivand, 1999b). In short, the New Deal has improved the labour market integration of young unemployed people in particular, but many (particularly older) people return to benefit receipt.

The above figures seem to justify questions about the main thrust of British labour market policy. Undoubtedly, increasing the level of employment seems an appropriate policy in terms of its fiscal impact (raising tax revenue and decreasing public expenditure). Equally, and more relevant in the context of this publication, higher levels of employment participation might reduce one potential risk condition for suicide, i.e. unemployment.

However, by international standards, the level of employment is already fairly high in the UK. The employment rate is defined as the number of people in employment relative to the population aged between 15 and 64 years. Adjusting for hours worked and expressing each person employed in full-time equivalent terms, this measure shows that in the UK employment has only slightly increased between the mid 1980s and 1997, with the UK ranking above the EU average. However, irrespective of hours worked per week, the UK has the second highest level of labour market participation in the EU after Denmark (European Commission, 1998: 27). This suggests that labour market integration policies might reach limits, unless they are sustained by expanding public sector employment (as in Denmark or Sweden) - which is fairly unlikely.

Conclusion

Under the premise that a high level of employment and low unemployment reduces one of the risk factors for suicide, this paper has shown that employment has grown across the UK since 1993. However, there are strong geographical disparities and a higher share of households without anybody in paid work than the level of unemployment suggests. What is more, unemployment affects young men more than other groups, even though the relative size of younger people in unemployment compared with other age groups has declined. While unemployed young men tend to have a more recent experience of employment than women or older men, they also tend to return to the unemployment register more quickly.

As to people in work, the UK has a markedly high level of job insecurity. This is partly an outcome of the high job turnover rate and probably the British labour market which is less regulated than elsewhere in Europe. New Deal policies will not change the latter. Nevertheless, new labour market programmes introduced since 1998 have had a positive impact on the degree of labour market participation, particularly of young people. However, this effect has probably at least as much to do with the state of the labour market (growing employment) as with the design of policies. It remains to be seen whether, under different labour market conditions, New Deal policies will have lasting success in terms of their impact on employment, and social integration, of young and long-term unemployed people.

REFERENCES

Bivand P (1999a) 'Jobs figures reveal New Deal success.' *Working Brief.* April, Unemployment Unit, 22-23.

Bivand P (1999b) 'Ethnic inequality in New Deal jobs.' *Working Brief.* October, Unemployment Unit, 8-9.

Deacon A (1997) 'Benefit sanctions for the jobless: 'tough love' or rough treatment?' *Employment Policy Institute Economic Report*, 11, 7.

Department of Social security (DSS) (1998) *New Ambitions for Our Country: a New Contract for Welfare.* Cm 3805 London: The Stationery Office.

European Commission (1998) *Employment in Europe 1998.* D-G for Employment, Industrial Relations and Social Affairs, Luxembourg: Office for Official Publications of the European Communities.

Eurostat (1999) *Eurostatistics*, 7. Luxembourg: Office for Official Publications of the European Communities.

Finn D (1997) *The Stricter Benefit Regime and the New Deal for the Unemployed.* Paper presented at the Social Policy Association, 31st Annual Conference, University of Lincolnshire and Humberside, 15-17 June.

Finn D (1999) *From Full Employment to Full Employability: New Labour and the Unemployed.* Conference paper WS/69, European Forum, Florence: European University Institute, April 15/16.

Gallie D and Russell H (1998) Unemployment and life satisfaction. *Archives Européennes de Sociologie* XXXIX: 3-35.

Gregg P and Wadsworth J (1998) Unemployment and households: causes and consequences of employment polarisation among European countries. In: *MISEP Policies*, no. 63, Employment Observatory, Luxembourg: Office for Official Publications of the European Communities, pages 31-35.

Gunnell D, Lopatatzidis A, Dorling D, Wehner H, Jonathan H and Frankel S (1999) Suicide and unemployment in young people. Analysis of trends in England and Wales, 1921-1995. *British Journal of Psychiatry* 175: 263-270.

Kieselbach T, Beelmann G, Meyer R and Traiser U (1999) *Jugenarbeitslosigkeit und soziale Ausgrenzung in Deutschland.* National report within EU project 'Youth Unemployment and Social Exclusion', mimeo, University of Bremen.

Labour Market Trends (various years and issues). London: Office for National Statistics.

Moser K and Paul K (1999) *Arbeitslosigkeit und seelische Gesundheit, Metaanalysen.* Paper presented at symposium: Arbeitslosigkeit – Wege aus der Krise, University of Erlangen-Nurembourg.

Organisation for Economic Co-operation and Development (OECD) (1997) *Employment Outlook.* Paris: OECD.

Plant R (1998) 'So you want to be a citizen.' *New Statesman*, 6 February.

Smith R (1987) *Unemployment and Health: a Disaster and a Challenge.* Oxford: Oxford University Press.

Spencer P (1996) 'Reactions to a flexible labour market.' In R Jowell *et al.* (eds.) *British Social Attitudes: the 13ᵗʰ Report.* Dartmouth: Aldershot.

Teasdale P (1998) ncidence and repeat spells of unemployment: an analysis using claimant data.' *Labour Market Trends*, November, Office for National Statistics.

Turok I and Edge N (1999) *The Jobs Gap in Britain's Cities: Employment Loss and Labour Market Consequences.* Bristol: The Policy Press.

Warton R, Walker R and McKay S (1998) *Implementing 'Welfare to Work' in Britain: Evidence from Applied Research.* Mimeo, Loughborough University: Centre for Research in Social Policy.

Gill Jones

SUICIDE, RISK AND IDENTITY: PROBLEMS OF MASTERY IN THE MODERN WORLD?

Understanding the evidence: a sociological approach

We are all justifiably concerned about the rates of suicide among young men, and it is important that we should understand why these rates are apparently on the increase so that we can take preventive steps not just at an individual level - to alleviate individual sorrows - but also at a *societal* level. There are many reasons why young men may take their own lives, and during the course of the day we will hear a range of explanations proposed.

As with crime statistics and unemployment statistics, suicide statistics have to be examined carefully. The dramatic apparent increase in male suicide could be artefactual and the result of changes in the definition and measurement of suicide, or it could be real and reflect changes in the wider society. Suicides are 'social facts' (needing explanations in terms of other social facts) according to Durkheim (1897) who argued that suicide rates - being fairly constant, but varying between societies - had an existence beyond that of an individual suicide. So if we accept increasing suicide rates as 'real', then we should look for causal factors in the wider society.

I want to focus here on some of the social factors which might be affecting suicide rates, rather than psychological factors which will affect individual behaviour, although it will become apparent in the course of this paper that there is not always a clear distinction between the two. I want to look at some of the changes in the wider society that might impact on young men's sense of identity and belonging. My specific brief is to produce a sociological explanation which focuses on gender and family issues, drawing in part on my own research on how young people make their transitions into adulthood in the UK, and the kinds of problems they face as they 'grow up'.

Social Change

The increase in the suicide rate of young men needs to be seen in the context of a number of wider social trends. The first of these is that although standards of living, and quality of life, have improved over recent decades, there is still differential access to many of the new opportunities presented. While there are greater opportunities for young people to gain qualifications, there are fewer opportunities for work, especially manual work. Social networks remain an important means of 'getting in and getting on', but not everyone has access to social capital. As a society we have become more home-centred, but home is not necessarily a happy place, and many lack access to positive and supportive relationships in the family home. Though many aspects of industrial society are undergoing transformation, social divisions persist. Thus social class continues to affect family breakdown, access to education and jobs, and quality of life, and gender divisions persist both in the labour market and in the home. We are still a divided nation in terms of wealth and health, and risk and vulnerability are more focused at the bottom end of the social spectrum.

Transition to adulthood

Social change is rapid, and many of the problems experienced by young people nowadays are different from those faced by their parents' generation thirty years or so ago. Then, it may have been possible to have some kind of normative agreement about what constitutes the achievement of adulthood on the basis of changes in social and economic status in different areas of people's lives. Table 1 shows how the period of youth has been extended, driving a wedge between childhood and adulthood, creating a period characterised by transitional status and semi-dependence, and increasing the potential for risk. As a result of the extension of education and training, the loss of the youth labour market and the erosion of welfare benefits, youth has become a period in life when the young are unexpectedly thrown back onto dependence on their parents, having to delay any ambition they may have for independent adulthood. In welfare terms, youth extends until the mid-20s.

Table 1: Extended youth

Transition	Childhood	Youth	Adulthood
School to work	School	Course or scheme	Labour market?
Family	Child in family	Cohabiting with partner/ Single lone parent	Partner - Parent?
Household	Parental home	Intermediate household - eg with peers, kin or alone	Independent home?
Housing	Parent home-owner or council tenant?	Transitional housing - eg bedsitter, room in shared flat	Home-owner or council tenant?
Income	Child income	Youth income	Full adult income?
Economic independence	Dependence	Semi-dependence	Independence?

This is not the only problem. It is far less clear now when adulthood has been achieved. The 'destinations' of marriage, family formation, independent housing, and particularly a stable working career, are all subject to new risks and uncertainties. Apparent 'progress' may stall, as a job is lost or a relationship breaks down. So the notions of progress, of success and failure need to be re-appraised. We cannot easily identify what constitutes a successful transition to adulthood. Equally, and more importantly perhaps, we cannot easily identify and target the vulnerable during the extended period of youth.

I will focus for a moment on changes in the labour market and in family life which affect young people's transitions, and make some links between these changes and changes in rates and patterns of suicide.

Labour market

The extension of education has its down-side when we turn to the youth labour market, which has virtually collapsed (Table 2). Not only have the jobs traditionally occupied by young people, in the UK at least, disappeared, but the longer term prospects of a steady job and linear career are far less clear.

Table 2: Activities of 16/17 year-olds, 1989 and 1996, England and Wales

Main activity	1989 %	1996 %
Full-time education	48	72
Full-time job	23	7
Government training	24	12
No full-time activity	5	10

Source: Payne, 1998.

One of the effects of globalisation, as Jochen Clasen shows (see pages 31 - 47), is the geographical shift of manufacturing away from the industrialised west. Manual jobs in manufacturing have been lost in the UK and replaced with service industry jobs, tending to be non-manual and often part-time. This shift has arguably favoured women more than men, at least in term of the gendered distribution of occupations, as there has been a loss of traditionally 'masculine jobs'. There has been an increase in credentialism, and a decline in jobs not requiring qualifications. Young people without qualifications are finding it harder to get jobs, and those still entering the labour market are more likely to be entering low paid work than labour market entrants five or 10 years ago. Other than through the New Deal for 18-24 year olds, employers appear not to be recruiting young people, thus worsening their labour market positions. Unemployment persists, particularly affecting young men (Table 3). Youth incomes from all sources (eg wages under Minimum Wage legislation, Training allowances, Education Maintenance Allowances, Welfare Benefits) are held low, so that, for many, adulthood in policy terms is deferred until the mid-twenties.

Table 3: Unemployment rates (percent of all economically active) by sex and age, UK, 1991-97.

	1991 %	1993 %	1995 %	1997 %
Males				
16-19	16	22	20	18
20-24	15	20	17	14
25-44	8	11	9	7
All >16	9	12	10	8
Females				
16-19	13	16	15	14
20-24	10	12	11	9
25-44	7	7	7	5
All >16	7	8	7	6

Source: UK Labour Force Survey (ONS (1998), Table 4.25)

It seems, then, that young people who seek to enter the traditional working class routes to the labour market are being offered the educational and training alternative (which they may reject) or dead-end jobs, if they are lucky enough to get jobs at all. Unemployment, and even the fear or anticipation of unemployment, have been shown to be not only *associated* with suicide behaviour, but also *causal* factors affecting mental health (West and Sweeting, 1996). The gendered distribution of occupations, which previously mainly caused disadvantage among young women, now also hits unqualified young men, leaving them without status in the labour market.

Family life

There have also been changes in family life, affecting both the family of origin and the family which the individual will create. First, the increased labour market participation of women has resulted in challenges to traditional 'gender roles', including the loss of the male 'breadwinner role', and some evidence at least of a more equal (and less gendered) division of domestic labour (Charles and Kerr, 1999; Utting, 1995). The quality of family life may also have changed: research indicates an increased focus on companionate relationships involving greater gender equality rather than male domination (Finch and Summerfield, 1999).

Table 4: Family situation at age 16 by birth cohort

Birth Cohort	1931 - 45	1951 - 55	1971 - 74
Lived with both natural parents to age 16 - %	80	87	73
Parents separated or divorced lived with mother - %	4	5	19
Father deceased, lived with mother - %	4	4	1
Other - %	12	4	7
Total - %	100	100	100

Source: Kiernan et al., 1998 (based on 1991 Sexual Attitudes and Lifestyles Survey)

Family structures have also changed, with an increase in family breakdown. Young people are more likely to have experienced marital conflict and family breakdown (Table 4), and there is increased likelihood that they will experience breakdown of any partnership they themselves form, as family structures become more unstable. Many people are more tentative about family formation, extending the period of bachelorhood, delaying partnership and childbirth. Median ages at marriage and birth of first child (the factors that tend to be associated with 'settling down') are increasing (Utting, 1995), and family formation is no longer a clear indicator of adulthood.

How do these changes link with suicide? Stephen Platt (see pages 1 - 31) has identified the association between indicators of family stability and suicide behaviour. In a study of depression and suicidal behaviour among young people seeking help from The Samaritans, Katz *et al.* (1999) found an association with having an absent father, anxiety about parental relationships, and lack of emotional support. Pritchard (1995) calls suicide 'the ultimate rejection' and associates it with earlier childhood neglect and abuse, through problems of self-esteem, lack of love and affection, and hostility, though he is concerned not to overemphasise this link.

Family conflict and family breakdown increasingly threaten the security of the home environment in which young people are growing up. Durkheim argued that high suicide rates were linked with low levels of social solidarity. The term 'social capital' has become very popular of late: access to employment is often dependent on social networks, including family links with the labour market. Membership of a family which has poor links with the labour market affects unemployment, so that unemployment runs in families (Payne, 1987). Not all young people have good family relationships, or can use family networks, or obtain family support, or live in the parental home, all factors associated with ability to get a job after unemployment (Stafford *et al.*, 1999).

We can perhaps also link the increase in suicide with the loss of traditional (normative) gender roles in the home, with the increase in family insecurity, and the greater likelihood that men will be either single or divorced or separated from their partners. Furthermore, at a time when young people are increasingly forced into dependence on their parents, changes in family life have made this more problematic: many have no one to turn to.

Risk-taking and age

These changing transitions have led to a generalised increase in stress for young people, including increased health risk (Furlong and Cartmel, 1997). Young people have low mortality and morbidity rates in general, being one of the healthiest groups, but, as West and Sweeting (1996:50) indicate, 'the biggest obstacle of all to understanding the health needs of young people has been the assumption that adolescence and health go hand in hand'. Brannen *et al.* (1994: 69) show that young people have distinctive health problems, with deaths from both suicide and 'external' violence increasing, especially among young men. Table 5 indicates the predominance of injury and poisoning as causes of death among 15-24 year old men in particular. Rutter and Smith (1995) argue that mental health in children and adolescents, as indicated by crime, alcohol and drug abuse, depression, eating disorders, and suicidal behaviour, has deteriorated since World War II.

Table 5: Cause of death by age and sex, UK, 1998

Cause of death	1-14 years %	15-24 years %	25-34 years %	All ages %
Males				
Circulatory diseases	5	4	9	42
Cancer	16	7	10	27
Respiratory diseases	7	4	5	15
Injury and poisoning	*30*	*63*	*51*	*4*
Infectious diseases	8	2	5	1
Other	34	19	20	11
Females				
Circulatory diseases	6	7	12	43
Cancer	18	17	26	23
Respiratory diseases	7	5	6	16
Injury and poisoning	*23*	*43*	*28*	*2*
Infectious diseases	8	4	5	1
Other	37	24	24	15

Source: ONS (1998)

One of the effects of an extended transition to adulthood could well be an extended involvement with same-sex peer groups, which usually diminishes with stable employment and the formation of one-to-one partnerships. Studies of criminal behaviour among young people have examined the ways in which there is gradually desistence from crime as young people grow up, form adult relationships, and become less involved in same-sex peer group activities (eg Graham and Bowling, 1995). There could, therefore, be knock-on effects resulting from delayed family formation and the potential for extension of peer group involvement. Furlong and Cartmel (1997: 71) suggest that resulting peer pressures can lead young women to eating disorders, because of pressures to conform to group stereotypes of body images. Peer pressures may thus exacerbate gender differences.

Table 6: Self-reported current participation in offending by age and sex, England and Wales

Offence group	Males			Females		
	14-17 %	18-21 %	22-25 %	14-17 %	18-21 * %	22-25 %
Property offences	17	25	27	13	9	3
Violent offences	12	9	4	7	4	<1
Expressive offences	8	8	0	8	1	<1
All offences	24	31	31	19	11	4
Current drug use	17	47	31	17	17	22

Source: Graham and Bowling, 1995

Gender differences appear in suicidal behaviour, such as the apparently gendered contrast between actual and 'attempted' suicide, or between 'active' and 'passive' methods of suicide. Stephen Platt indicates (see Chapter 2) that active methods predominate among young men, and are becoming even more common.   While 'achieved' suicide is higher among males, attempted suicide is higher among females.   According to the Samaritans, four-fifths of suicides are among males, but four-fifths of attempted suicide are among females.   The distinction between the two may be misleading: attempted suicide is sometimes referred to as a 'cry for help' but one study in the US which followed up attempted suicides over a ten-year period showed that 6% eventually killed themselves (Cullberg *et al.,* 1988, quoted in Pritchard, 1995).

Suicide is one form of deliberate self-harm, also associated with accidents, drug and alcohol abuse, eating disorders, and psychiatric problems, and appears to be at one end of a continuum of risk-behaviour.   Risk-taking behaviours which affect health, such as smoking, drinking, drug-taking and unprotected sex, are often associated with youth (Brannen *et al.,* 1994), and health interventions tend to focus on these.   However, risk-taking can however also perform an important social function and it to this that I now turn.

Emerging themes

I want to explore two aspects of these changes in more depth: the first is the issue of risk and uncertainty; the second concerns the increasing challenges to traditional working class masculinity. In both cases, we can consider the ways in which young people may try to gain (or claim) control of situations over which they have very little control, ways which may be to do with survival, but on occasion may also result in oppression of those who are even more vulnerable.

Uncertainty, risk and mastery

One current sociological argument is that it is the social conditions of late modernity, described as *The Risk Society* (Beck, 1992), which make youth such a difficult part of the life course. Risk and uncertainty are not just 'out there', in the wider society, but are also internalised in individual and group behaviour.

The sociological explanation refers to the problems of coping with the uncertainties of identity, status, emerging independence, and of moving towards an uncertain future. In the post-industrial 'risk societies', the structures of modernity, structures (of both inequality and of solidarity), such as the labour market, the family, communities, social class solidarities, are breaking down. As a result, people have been individualised, left to their own devices to work out their biographies, lacking a blueprint or template to follow. This affects everyone, but perhaps young people who are just beginning to decide how to lead their lives more than their parents, who have already embarked on this uncertain future. I noted earlier that youth now is different from youth a generation ago, with the result that parents are not necessarily in a position to help.

According to Giddens (1991), our biographies are far more uncertain than they were at the start of this century, and the future is an unknown. Individuals construct narratives of self-identity, which have to be continually revised. Giddens calls these 'reflexive biographies' and argues that 'the universe of future events is open to be shaped by human intervention' (1991:109). This loss of certainty can be threatening. According to Giddens (1991: 137), 'the deskilling of day-to-day life is an alienating and fragmenting phenomenon so far as the self is concerned'. However, among the powerless, there are some survivors, and Giddens identifies a survival mentality (1991:193):

> A 'survivor' is someone who feels deprived of adequate social mastery in a threatening series of personal and social environments. Yet a survivalist outlook carries connotations of appropriation as well as powerlessness. Someone who concentrates on surviving in personal relations, as in other spheres of life, cannot be said to have abandoned all autonomy over his or her life's circumstances. *Even if only in a somewhat negative sense, the individual clearly seeks active mastery: to survive is to be able in a determined way to ride out the trials life presents and overcome them.* (Giddens, 1991: 193, my emphasis).

Giddens suggests that risk-taking can be seen as a means of taking control of the future ('colonising the future'), but at the same time it 'opens up new settings of risk' - such as gambling or life-risking behaviours (1991: 117).

While adulthood represents an uncertain future, youth is heavily structured by policies constraining what young people do, as well as increasing opportunities. Opportunities for experimentation, risk-taking behaviour or individual solutions are limited. The New Deal, for example, is tightly structured, while more and more benefits are conditional and based on contractual obligations (following the principles of 'workfare'). Opportunities for economic independence have been taken away (Jones and Bell, 2000). Young people are thus forced into situations of extended dependence on their parents or carers, which may be fine as long as their parents or carers are willing and able to continue to care for them and provide them with economic support, and as long as young people are willing to postpone autonomy and independence. Young people may justifiably feel they have little room for movement and that their choices are limited. The political rhetoric is about citizenship and participation, but young people are in many respects excluded from participation in the adult world.

The powerlessness experienced by some young men lies in part in the policy structures which very (and increasingly) tightly control what they are able to do; it lies in the diminishing supply of working class male jobs; and it lies in the changing labour market participation of women, and the resulting shifts to the traditional gendered division of labour in the home which allowed masculinity to hold sway in the domestic sphere. Feelings of powerlessness and lack of control are very contrary to the assertions of power traditionally bound up with masculinity, which is thus challenged at every turn.

Young people who feel they have no control over their lives may nevertheless claim responsibility for their actions in a process of 'creative redefinition' (Breakwell, 1986). The less autonomy young people actually have, the more they may feel the need to take risks and claim responsibility. In a study of young people leaving home, I explored perceptions of risk (Jones, 1995, 1997). Leaving home is a way of asserting adult identity, if it works, and the following comment makes the point succinctly.

> I wanted just a bit of freedom so that I could make my own choice. But my choices were getting made for me, so I wanted to say: "Right. OK, I'll make that decision." And most of the time it was the wrong decision, and I learned from my mistakes, but if I could make that mistake myself that was fine. It was my mistake. I made it. (Patricia, aged 22, quoted in Jones, 1997).

It is significant to our concerns today that young people, despite their powerlessness, attempt to retain, or at least claim, responsibility for their actions. One study has suggested that young people regarded even suicide in terms of individual rights, in contrast to their parents who judged suicide in religious and moral terms (Hill, 1996). This suggests to me that young people individualise the problems which lead to suicide, and may regard suicide as the outcome of choice. In a similar vein, Brannen *et al.* (1994:74) found that young people were less likely than their parents to believe that luck, rather than individual control, played a part in their health.

Balint (1959), quoted in Giddens (1991:132), suggests that the thrill of risk-taking activities involves 'awareness of exposure to danger, a voluntary exposure to danger, and the more or less confident expectation of overcoming it'. Although he was commenting on risk-taking in general, we can apply these points to suicide as well, and should consider: level of consciousness (whether alcohol or drug induced), level of voluntarism (whether pushed by violence or victimisation) and level of expectation of actual death (including in cases of 'attempted' suicide). In Giddens's terms, how much 'mastery' do people have over their own suicidal actions? In other words, should we be exploring suicide behaviour as a rather extreme attempt to take control and assert autonomy, an act of 'mastery' from a position otherwise defined as powerless?

Masculinities: challenges and responses

I have tried to show why young people might be at risk, and risk suicide. The next question is why especially young men, and the term 'mastery' leads me neatly into gender issues.

Men are under pressure these days, and studies of the construction of masculinities in the modern world can help us understand why. Male heterosexual identity has been described as a 'highly fragile socially constructed phenomenon' (Mac an Ghaill, 1994:9), constructed in relation to, and against, femininity and subordinated forms of masculinity (eg homosexuality). The traditional notion of masculinity has been challenged by feminism and homosexuality, and it has been argued that one recent response to these challenges has been an over-emphasis on a dominant form of masculinity characterised by heterosexuality, power, authority, aggression and technical competence (Connell, 1987; Mac an Ghaill, 1994:12).

Connell (1987) locates gender structures in the division of labour, in power relations between men and women, and in sexuality. Similarly, according to Beck (1992: 112):

> In the stereotypical male gender role as
> 'career man', economic individualisation
> and masculine role behaviour are joined

together. ... In the context of male life, fatherhood and career, economic independence and familial life are not contradictions that have to be fought for and held together against the conditions in the family and society; instead their compatibility with the traditional male role is prescribed and protected.

There is no conflict between public and private lives for men, who (unlike women) can easily accommodate their traditional normative roles at work and at home. Men therefore do not necessarily want to be 'liberated' from their role as the breadwinner and head of the family, or from the perpetuation of a gendered domestic division of labour (which affirms masculinity). But there are challenges to the traditional male role both in the home as well as in the labour market, as we have seen. Some people cope with these changes by adapting, others hang on to tradition and try to repress change. Thus we have the concepts of the New Man, who shares or purports to share domestic tasks, and the New Lad!

In general, studies of youth subcultures in the 1970s tended to ignore ways in which these were linked with the oppression of women and with racism. However, according to Hearn (1996:203):

an overemphasis on masculinity and a neglect of social relations between men and women can lead to a redefinition of men as victims of historical, cultural and gendered processes, to which men are bound. Similarly, in this view, women may easily be blamed for men's problems.

Canaan (1996) studied young white working class male groups, which associated drinking and fighting with a particular stereotype of masculinity. She highlights the role of peer pressure on younger men to prove 'hardness' through sex behaviour, drinking and violence. Thus, individual control can be lost in the face of peer pressure and alcohol, and aggression can be both a response to powerlessness and an abuse of differential power.

Physical and verbal bullying at school are said to be a cause of suicide (Katz *et al.*, 1999; Marland, 1992, quoted in Mac an Ghaill, 1994). At school, doing academic work or having girls as friends (rather than as sexual partners) can be seen as effeminate, and so an anti-school culture develops which values a particular type of masculinity, places a high value on manual labour (as Willis (1977) found back in the 1970s), and bullies those who do not conform to this image even when this is an image now more difficult to sustain. Similarly, Thurston (1996: 146) describes his study of prison as a masculising agency, producing tough and aggressive forms of masculinity, within which some constantly defined themselves in terms of their heterosexuality by referring to their wives or girlfriends, while 'others' who did not conform to this typing were subjected to abuse and violence. He comments that, when an attempt was made to make the atmosphere less oppressive, suicide rates went down.

There is, therefore, some pressure on young men to assert their masculinity, although this is becoming increasingly difficult both in the workplace and in the home. It can be difficult for those who do not sign up to this kind of masculinity. In the case of young men, the reinvention of masculinities (which exclude and pick on the 'different', the 'non-conformist'), is accompanied by an increase in risk-taking behaviours, with variations in the levels of awareness and control. Katz *et al* (1999) also identified gender issues affecting suicidal behaviour among young men, including the emphasis on asserting masculinity, and against gender equality. They also argue that young men can view seeking help seen as a sign of weakness which they would therefore resist.

Implications

If we are to understand why more young men are committing suicide, our explanations can start here. Suicide behaviour forms part of an increasing need for risk-taking, on the one hand, and an increasing apparent need for victimisation, on the other hand, among young men who are having to cope with new uncertainties, including new challenges to their masculinity and the status of men in the modern world.

The paper raises some issues for suicide prevention strategies:

- There are dangers in targeting and individualising provision when vulnerability is harder to identify: all young people are potentially at risk

- There is a need to support parents and particularly to inform them about the current problems faced by young people (which are probably different from their own experiences), so that parents are better able to support their children through the period of youth

- There is a need to change, through education, public attitudes to 'difference', and to create an atmosphere of tolerance, particularly in institutions such as schools and prisons

- There is a need to questions definitions of success and failure in youth, and to understand young people's own criteria

- The idea that seeking help is a sign of weakness and failure needs to be addressed.

REFERENCES

Balint M (1959) *Thrills and Regressions.* London: Hogarth.

Beck U (1992) *Risk Society: Towards a New Modernity.* London: Sage.

Brannen J, Dodd K, Oakley A and Storey P (1994) *Young People, Health and Family Life.* Buckingham: Open University Press.

Breakwell G (1986) *Coping with Threatened Identities.* London: Methuen.

Canaan JE (1996) "One thing leads to another": drinking, fighting and working class masculinities In: M Mac an Ghaill (ed.), *Understanding Masculinities: Social relations and Cultural Arenas.* Buckingham: Open University Press.

Charles N and Kerr M (1999) Women's work. In G Allan (ed.) *The Sociology of the Family: A Reader.* Oxford: Blackwell.

Connell RW (1987) *Gender and Power.* Cambridge: Polity.

Cullberg J, Wasserman D and Stefansson CG (1988) Who commits suicide after a suicide attempt? *Acta Psychiatrica Scandinavica* 77: 598-603.

Durkheim E [1897] (1952) *Suicide.* London: Routledge and Kegan Paul.

Finch J and Summerfield P (1999) Social reconstruction and the emergence of companionate marriage. In: G Allan (ed.) *The Sociology of the Family: A Reader.* Oxford: Blackwell.

Furlong A and Cartmel F (1997) *Youth and Social Change.* Buckingham: Open University Press.

Giddens A (1991) *Modernity and Self-Identity: Self and Society in the Late Modern Age.* Cambridge: Polity.

Graham J and Bowling B (1995) *Young People and Crime.* Home Office Research Study 145. London: Home Office.

Hearn J (1996) Is masculinity dead? A critique of the concept of masculinity/masculinities. In: M. Mac an Ghaill (ed.) *Understanding Masculinities: Social Relations and Cultural Arenas.* Buckingham: Open University Press.

Hill K (1996) *The Long Sleep: Young People and Suicide.* London: Virago.

Jones G (1995) *Leaving Home.* Buckingham: Open University Press.

Jones G (1997) Youth homelessness and the 'underclass'. In: R MacDonald (ed.) *Youth, the 'Underclass' and Social Exclusion.* London: Routledge.

Jones G and Bell R (2000) *Balancing Acts: Youth, Parenting and Public Policy.* York: Joseph Rowntree Foundation.

Katz A, Buchanan A and McCoy A (1999) *Young Men Speak Out.* London: Samaritans.

Kiernan K, Land H and Lewis J (1998) *Lone Parenthood.* Oxford: Clarendon Press.

Mac an Ghaill M (1994) *The Making of Men: Masculinities, Sexualities and Schooling.* Buckingham: Open University Press.

Marland M (1992) When words can kill. *The Guardian,* 2 June, page 20.

Office of National Statistics (ONS) (1998) *Social Trends 28.* London: The Stationery Office.

Payne J (1987) Does unemployment run in families? *Sociology* 2: 199-214.

Payne J (1998) *Routes at Sixteen: Trends and Choices in the Nineties.* DfEE Research Report No 55.

Pritchard C (1995) *Suicide - The Ultimate Rejection?* Buckingham: Open University Press.

Rutter M and Smith D (1995) *Psychosocial Disorders in Young People.* Chichester: John Wiley.

Stafford B, Heaver C, Ashworth K, Bates C, Walker R, McKay S and Trickey H (1999) *Work and Young Men.* York, Joseph Rowntree Foundation.

Thurston R (1996) Are you sitting comfortably? Men's storytelling, masculinities, prison culture and violence. In: M Mac an Ghaill (ed.) *Understanding Masculinities: Social Relations and Cultural Arenas.* Buckingham: Open University Press.

Utting D (1995) *Family and Parenthood.* York: Joseph Rowntree Foundation.

West P and Sweeting H (1996) Nae job, nae future: young people and health in the context of unemployment. *Health and Social Care in the Community* 4: 50-62.

Willis P (1977) *Learning to Labour: How Working Class Kids Get Working Class Jobs.* Aldershot: Gower.

Richard Holloway

SHIFTS IN CULTURE, VALUES AND RELIGION

The end of tradition

The difficulty that many of us face today is that we find ourselves spiritually homeless, or semi-detached. We are no longer comfortably and unselfconsciously established at the heart of any of the great traditions. And it is with the nature of tradition itself that I want to start. There are a number of formulas that try to capture the atmosphere of our society in the final months of the second millennium, but the one that I think is the simplest and easiest to expound is the end of tradition: ours is a post-traditional society. A tradition is a system of ideas and practices based on a set of assumptions or premises from which a complex social or religious structure has evolved. These structures have traditionally acted as containers for humanity. Post-traditional society is a highly complex phenomenon, and its herald and celebrant was Nietzsche, but I do not want to engage with the philosophical aspects of the phenomenon; instead, I want to focus on some of the structural or cultural elements.

The first of these is *globalisation*. We are familiar with this term as a description of the economic system that dominates the world. It is called the global market economy and, whatever we think of it, we all have to acknowledge that it has bonded the world together in a new way, so that an economic crisis in Tokyo or Jakarta has immediate effects in London or New York. We are familiar with the idea of the world as a global village, but it is a mistake to limit this metaphor to the economic system. It has profoundly affected the religious and intellectual currencies in the world, as well as the economic systems. Apart from anything else that might be said about them, we are now aware of other systems and traditions, other paradigms, using that term to mean 'an entire constellation of beliefs, values, techniques which are shared by the members of a particular community', to quote Thomas Kuhn (Kuhn, 1962), the originator of paradigm theory. We have got so used to this kind of liberal recognition of the claims of other human systems that we easily forget how new it is. Paradigms or traditions operate at their best when we are completely unaware that we are in one. *Our* paradigm is not an arbitrary human construct, the way *we* happen to do things; it is the way things actually *are*. This is why, for instance, when the European colonists encountered the very different paradigms or world views held by the native peoples in north, central and south America, they dismissed them as primitive, devilish and inherently without any value. This spiritual arrogance and lack of imagination was the prelude to the horrifying genocide and destruction of ancient cultures that characterised European colonisation in the Americas as well as in Australia. The irony is that today, in our own spiritually confused culture, we are turning back to some of the traditions our forebears tried to eradicate, because they contain great wisdom, not least in their attitude to the earth and their reverence for creation.

Globalisation makes it impossible for us to be unaware of other traditions, other ways of looking at the world. The resulting shift in attitude is what we call pluralism. Indeed, *plural society*, rather than *post-traditional society*, might be a more accurate description of the situation we are in today. In many ways, ours is a multi-traditional society, but the very experience of encountering other cultures, other paradigms, has had an inevitably eroding effect on the way in which traditions are held. The term that is used to describe this process of cultural erosion is *relativism*, and there are two subtly different meanings to the term. One is descriptive: as a matter of fact, it says, your tradition or cultural paradigm is relative to your context and its inherited perspective. For instance, if you were born in Ireland, the chances are that you'll be a Catholic; if you were born in Turkey, the chances are that you'll be a Moslem; if you were born in India, the chances are that you'll be a Hindu. But a subtler form of relativism would go on to say that the points of view themselves are all relative and there is no way in which we can say that any one of them is superior to any other.

Many people find this kind of society induces enormous anxiety in them, because it has shifted all the landmarks that once guided us and made us feel we knew where we were. So let me look now at some of the responses to the situation we are in. One of the most fascinating of responses is *fundamentalism.*   Anthony Giddens defines fundamentalism as 'defending tradition in the traditional way'. An illustration might help us to make the point. Take the monarchy: this is one of our oldest traditional systems. If you were asked to justify the retention of the monarchy today, you'd probably offer a number of pragmatic arguments: you'd say it was a valuable symbol of the continuity of the nation or that it was good for the tourist trade or for British exports. A monarchical fundamentalist, however, would scorn these attempts to rationalise the office and would point, instead, to the divine right of kings to rule over us. In other words, the fundamentalist defends tradition in the traditional way, and refers to original assumptions as though they were valid for all time and required no new justification. In periods of accelerating social change, fundamentalism is an obvious refuge, and its refusal to negotiate with the new consciousness is both a strength and a weakness. When you engage in dialogue with fundamentalism you soon discover that no real negotiation is possible. Indeed, Giddens offers *refusal to negotiate* as another definition of fundamentalism.   The tragic paradox of fundamentalism is that its very intransigence and refusal to negotiate new uses and meanings for tradition ends by placing tradition itself in great jeopardy. Fundamentalism is one of the most dangerously volatile elements in our world, ranging from the wilder reaches of the Christian Right in the USA to the excesses of the Taliban in Afghanistan.

Another response to the confusions of our era is absolute moral and religious scepticism. I suspect that absolute moral scepticism is rarely found in its pure form, but as an intellectual theory it holds that things simply are as they are and there is nothing we can do about them. We are determined by factors entirely beyond our control and the work of the intellect is largely descriptive, telling how people behave in all their variety. This approach is the polar opposite of fundamentalism, though, in a mischievous way, it often colludes with it, because the cultured despisers of religion prefer it to be heroically obscurantist and opposed to all development and evolution. We live in a time when the arch-priests of secular consciousness dismiss all religion as irrational, just as the dominant forms of religion are celebrating the triumph of that same irrationalism.

How is the liberal mind to respond to this brutal polarisation between those who believe that religious tradition presents us with a fixed script, and those who dismiss all religious and moral traditions as superstitious remnants of infantile irrationality? I would like to suggest a musical metaphor to help us forward. I got it from John Saxbee, the Bishop of Ludlow. He describes an experience Michael Ives, the American composer, had when he was a young man. He was listening to a record on the phonograph in the family parlour when he heard a brass band going past outside in the street, and realised he was hearing both tunes at once. His compositions employ the same technique. Saxbee suggests that the liberal minded Christian has to listen to two tunes if she is to be faithful to her own integrity as a modern believer. Those of us who try to follow this way find ourselves listening to the tradition and to the culture and thought of our own day. We are hearing two tunes, sometimes discordantly, and we want to try to be faithful to both. We believe that it is possible to use tradition in a contemporary or living way; but it is a fairly taxing way to live, and it is not susceptible of the kind of simplifications that religious traditions need if they are to commend themselves to busy people. Whatever we make of this brief analysis, we would probably all agree that our society now lacks a single, unifying religious or mythic tradition. Instead, we inhabit a spiritual supermarket in which we have to make choices, and choice itself breeds insecurity. The value of the traditional paradigms was that, for most people, they did not involve much choice: they were the way things were. Even if we rebelled against them, we knew what we were up against. Today, no single myth or tradition encloses us, and we all have to do what seems right in our own eyes. It is hardly surprising, therefore, that ours is an anxious, depressive society. Nietzsche thought that religion was created to deal with human depression; it is ironic that, just as we are getting most depressed, religion has lost its power to help. Here is what Nietzsche (1899) said:

> ...the main concern of all great religions has been to fight a certain weariness and heaviness grown to epidemic proportions...from time to time and in certain parts of the earth a *feeling of physiological inhibition* is almost bound to seize on large masses of people, though, owing to their lack of physiological knowledge, they do not diagnose it as such: its cause and remedy are sought and tested only in the psychological-moral domain (this is my most general formula for what is usually called *"religion"*)...This dominating sense of displeasure is combated by means that reduce the feeling of life in general to its lowest point. If possible, will and desire are abolished altogether; all that produces affects and "blood" is avoided; no love; no hate; indifference; no revenge; no wealth; no work; one begs; if possible, no women, or as little as possible; in spiritual matters, Pascal's principle *il faut s'abêtir/one must make oneself stupid* is applied. The result, expressed in moral-psychological terms, is "selflessness", "sanctification"; in physiological terms: hypnotization - the attempt to win for man an approximation to what in certain animals is *hibernation*, in many tropical plants *estivation*, the minimum metabolism at which life will still subsist without really entering consciousness. An astonishing amount of human energy has been expended to this end...

Just when we are most in need of the religious narcotic, the supply drops!

Richard Holloway

The Revolutions of our Time

Related to the erosion of tradition is the revolutionary impact of social and industrial change in our society in the last twenty years. One of the most searching diagnosticians of the human condition was Karl Marx. Dr Marx was a lousy therapist, and no society today really tries to follow his prescriptions; but his diagnosis of human social pathology is still powerful and searching. His main insights, like most brilliant perceptions, once you get hold of them, are startlingly simple. The central claim is that power always justifies itself, not necessarily by brute force, though it is rarely reluctant to do that, but by theories or ideas. That is why the ruling ideas in any era always justify the position of the ruling class: they are always used to legitimate the way things are done by the people in charge. If we can accept the claim, if only for the sake of argument, that ruling elites always consolidate their position by creating a doctrinal justification for it in society as a whole, how does social evolution ever occur? Where does the impetus to move on and challenge accepted values come from? Hegel would have answered that the spirit of history itself, the mystical reality that animates the whole of time, evolves gradually towards human liberty. Marx borrowed the evolutionary idea, but said that it worked itself out through changes in the means of production, creating greater social complexity and an accompanying misery and despair that provoked challenge and change. Now, you don't have to buy the mysticism to recognise that history has, in fact, worked out like that.

Ruling elites always disguise their own self-interest in the language of theory and necessity. That's the main point I want to make here. An interesting example is provided by Kenneth Galbraith in his book, *The Good Society* (Galbraith, 1996). He writes of modern global capitalism: 'There is the inescapable fact that the modern market economy accords wealth and distributes income in a highly unequal, socially adverse and also functionally damaging fashion.' Galbraith is well aware of the efficacy of the market economy at generating wealth, but he is concerned at the way those who benefit from the system refuse to address the damaging effects it has on the most vulnerable members

of society. Thoughtful people ought to be concerned about the effects
of the global market economy on human communities. Most
unprejudiced thinkers would acknowledge the failures as well as the
successes of the global market economy. Few people today argue for its
complete abolition. Increasingly, however, people are calling for a
candid acknowledgement of its failures. And the main fact we have to
acknowledge is that the system that has made most of us more
prosperous has plunged a significant proportion of our fellow citizens
into poverty and despair.

One of the most tragically enduring facts of the history of human
industry is that change in the methods of production always has a
disproportionate impact upon the most vulnerable in society. History,
like nature, seems to be indifferent to the pain it causes the weak. Think
of the way the industrial revolution chewed up and spat out generations
of the poor, before we learned how to protect them from its worst
depredations. The paradox of our time is that it is the death of heavy
industry that is now devastating the poor. Much of this is the
consequence of global economic changes, coupled with the closure of
pits and defence industries. Heavy industry has been replaced by the
knowledge economy, and we are only now trying to catch up with its
consequential impact upon the poor and ill-educated. And, as if that
were not enough, social change has combined with the economic
revolution to destroy the cultural cohesion of the most vulnerable
sections of our society. When the culture revolutions of the Sixties met
and married the economic revolution of the Eighties, there was created a
potent instrument of social change that has transformed the social
landscape of Britain, and its most devastating impact has been upon
young, ill-educated workless males. The institutions that once gave
them a motive for responsible living, such as holding down a tough,
demanding job with its own culture and honour, and presiding, however
clumsily, within a marriage and family that was the primary context for
the nurture and socialising of children, have largely disappeared, and
with them the main ways the human community traditionally disciplined
and integrated what the Prayer Book calls 'the unruly wills and
affections of sinful men'. This shattering of the structures that once

gave the poor significance and purpose has created a breeding ground for despair. Whenever I refer to these facts in certain circles someone inevitably points out that no one in Britain is starving today, because absolute poverty has been eradicated. That may be technically true, but minority poverty has an exclusionary cruelty that is all its own. When most people were poor there was a camaraderie and cultural cohesion in belonging to the working class that gave them a strength and pride that transcended the structures that excluded them. But in a society where most people are prosperous, and the poor are a minority whose culture has disintegrated, the pain and anger they feel is heightened.

Conclusion

I have offered you a very broad interpretation of the topic I was given to talk about, 'shifts in culture, values and religion'. I have suggested that a number of powerful forces in our time have eroded traditional religious and ethical systems; and, at the same time, economic change and social revolution have destroyed the cultural cohesion of the most vulnerable sections of our society. So the paradox is that, just when we have created the kind of climate of insecurity and human depression that religion systems were evolved to deal with, the religious systems themselves are in crisis. My own hunch, and I take no pleasure in offering it, is that the tough, harshly defined religions probably offer to the vulnerable or confused the best protection from the storms of our time; while the more evolved religious systems may only add to the prevailing sense of insecurity, by the high premium they place upon tolerance and rationality. So (Chesterton, 1920),

> I tell you naught for your comfort,
> Yea, naught for your desire,
> Save that the sky grows darker yet
> And the sea rises higher.

Richard Holloway

REFERENCES

Chesterton GK (1920) *The Ballad of the White Horse*, book ii. London: Methuen.

Galbraith K (1996) *The Good Society: The Humane Agenda.* Boston: Houghton Mifflin Co.

Kuhn T (1962) *The Structure of Scientific Revolutions.* Chicago: Chicago University Press.

Neitzsche F (1899) A *Genealogy of Morals*, third essay, section 17. London: T Fisher Unwin.

SUICIDE IN YOUNG MEN: SERVICE-BASED OPPORTUNITIES FOR PREVENTION

Introduction

Platt (see pages 1 - 30) demonstrates that rates of suicide have risen sharply in men in Scotland over the last quarter of a century. This paper discusses the evidence that changes to services have contributed to this increase, and reviews the extent to which interventions by the caring services can be expected to reduce deaths by suicide.

Mental Illness

People suffering from mental ill-health are at greater risk of suicide than are the general population. Harris and Barraclough (1997) have produced a systematic review and meta-analysis[1] of the association between suicide and experience of mental illness. Their results are presented as Standardised Mortality Ratios (SMRs). SMRs take into account differences in age and gender structure between different populations, and so allow comparisons to be made. An SMR of 100 indicates the population average: an SMR of 150, by comparison, would be 50% higher than the average, and an SMR of 50 would be 50% lower than the average. A 95% confidence interval shows the degree of statistical uncertainty. For example, if the SMR was 120 with a Confidence Interval (CI) of 110 – 130, then there would be 19 chances out of 20 that the true value lay between 110 and 130, with 120 being the most likely value. Table 1 below shows examples of SMRs for suicide associated with mental ill-health.

Table 1: Standardised mortality ratios (SMRs) for suicide

Mental disorder or situation	Standardised mortality ratio (SMR)	95% confidence interval
History of self-poisoning	4070	3700-4467
In-patient in a psychiatric hospital	582	545–621
Long-stay in-patients (all diagnoses)	255	190–335
Major depression	2035	1827–2259
Schizophrenia	845	798–895
Anxiety disorders	1000	457-1898

Source: Harris and Barraclough 1997

There is an important difference between relative risk and population attributable risk. People are at much higher risk of suicide after deliberate self-harm than are the general population, but the actual number of people who harm themselves remains low with less than three percent dying by suicide by 13 years after deliberate self-harm (Hall *et al.*, 1998). SMRs are similar to relative risk, in that they show the risk of suicide compared to the general population. It is also important to know what proportion of all deaths by suicide can be related to these various risk factors. Studies in the 1970s concluded that up to 70% of people who killed themselves had been suffering from a depressive illness (Barraclough *et al.*, 1974) . Other studies have found lower figures. Foster *et al.* (1999) reported that 36% of a group of 117 people who died by suicide in Northern Ireland had a depressive disorder at the time of their death, compared to 4% of controls. In a study of people aged under 35years dying by suicide in Manchester Appleby *et al.* (1999) found that 23% had a major affective disorder[2], and a further 2% had mild depression, compared to 2% and 6% in controls respectively.

In work from the 1970s, depressive illnesses were commonly associated with death by suicide. Fombonne (1994) reviewed information on depression prevalence from epidemiological surveys and concluded that, despite differences in method, findings by various authors were suggestive of an increase in depressive disorders. This increase was greatest in younger birth cohorts[3]. This was largely similar to the findings of the Cross-National Collaborative Group, who reviewed a number of studies from different continents (Cross-National Collaborative Group, 1992). They concluded that depression was increasing, and that it began earlier in a person's life in successive birth cohorts on average. It is possible that these increases are artefactual[4], but the consistency of the findings does lend some support to the view that depression rates are increasing. Women have higher rates of depression than men, although some recent work suggests that this excess may be decreasing. Doris *et al.* (1999) speculate that changes in employment patterns may underlie this finding, relating the apparent increase in male depression to the rise in male suicides.

Some recent studies provide greater details of young people who have killed themselves. The process of re-constructing events leading up to a suicide, and in assessing the presence or absence of mental ill-health, is known as a psychological autopsy or post-mortem. These methods, while valuable, have inherent limitations because of their retrospective nature[5]. While reporting that acute and severe mental disorders were considerably more common in young people dying by suicide, Appleby *et al.* (1999) noted that chronic behavioural disturbances, rootlessness and social withdrawal, and both chronic and recent interpersonal problems, were also found more often. In a factor analysis, the interpersonal problems and acute, severe, psychiatric illness appeared particularly important. The authors conclude that 'there is no single solution to the rise in suicide in young people…both social and health measures could be beneficial' (Appleby *et al.*, 1999: 172). This theme will be revisited below.

Mental Health Services in Scotland

There has a been a substantial move in services, away from provision in institutions and towards services provided in a person's local community. The number of NHS psychiatric in-patient beds has declined rapidly. The total number of NHS beds decreased from 20,196 in 1965 to 16,467 in 1983 (Scottish Home and Health Department, 1985). By 1998 there were around 4000 adult mental health beds in Scotland (Accounts Commission for Scotland, 1999). The decline is not quite as precipitous as it appears, as the earlier figures include beds used for older people with mental health problems, while the Accounts Commission figure excludes beds designated for psychiatry of old age.

Despite the reduction in in-patient beds, a substantial resource is still invested in these services. Statutory agencies in Scotland spend around £320 million per year on mental health-related services, of which 79% is spent within the NHS (Accounts Commission for Scotland, 1999). The NHS spend includes £204 million devoted to specialist mental health services. Of the NHS specialist service total, 78% is spent on in-patient services (Accounts Commission for Scotland, 1999). The Accounts Commission also note substantial variations between areas and services.

Despite public concern about decreases in the number of in-patient beds, in-patient services are sometimes regarded with considerable suspicion. The Sainsbury Centre for Mental Health (1998) paints a bleak picture of acute psychiatric in-patient care in England. Half of a group of people studied by the Centre stated that they had not received enough information about their illness and possible treatments. People treated as in-patients reported little contact with staff other than doctors or nurses. There was substantial boredom on wards, and limited success in meeting people's long-term needs. There is no comparable evidence for Scotland, and it should be noted that mental state had generally improved by the time people left hospital in the English study.

Can the combination of the Sainsbury findings of limited quality in-patient services, combined with an overall reduction in in-patient beds and move to a community service, explain rising suicide rates? Geddes and Juzsczak (1995) and Geddes *et al.* (1997) have explored patterns of suicide after discharge from psychiatric hospitals in Scotland (see Stark *et al.*, 1995 for comments). They confirmed that people had a substantially higher risk of suicide in the period after discharge, compared to the general population (see Figure 1). This risk, in the year after discharge, was around 27 times the population average for men, and 40 times for women (Geddes *et al.*, 1997). Compared to work by Goldacre *et al.* (1993) in Oxford, the Scottish group had lower suicide rates in the first 28 days after discharge, but similar rates over the rest of the first year. SMRs were highest for diagnoses of personality disorder, non-psychotic depression and alcohol dependence in women, and for non-psychotic depression, personality disorder and affective psychoses in men (Geddes *et al.*, 1997). In both men and women, most deaths were in people aged between 25 and 64 years.

Geddes *et al.* (1997) re-analysed their results to take into account the changing suicide rates in the general population. They concluded that female suicide rates after hospital discharge best fitted a pattern of a fairly constant rate of suicide in the twelve months after discharge in the time period they examined, together with a declining population rate. Suicides after hospital discharge therefore made up a greater proportion of suicides in women. In men by contrast, there was a small increase over time in suicide in the year after hospital discharge, but which 'occurred in the presence of a much larger increase in the rate of suicide in the general male population, particularly in young men'. The work of Geddes *et al.* (1997) suggests that, while changes to in-patient practices are associated with some female suicides, they cannot be used to explain the increase in suicides among younger men.

There may, however, be opportunities to intervene in people recently discharged from psychiatric hospitals. Stark *et al.* (1994) examined deaths by suicide in Scotland in 1990-91 using the Scottish linked data set[6]. They found that 9.5% of men and 18.4% of women dying by suicide in those years had been in-patients in the year prior to their death. The length of stay during the previous admission had been generally brief (median length of stay 1-2 weeks). While this does not rule out the possibility that these individuals may have spent time in long-term psychiatric care in the past[7], it does indicate that the deaths did not occur immediately after leaving long-term care. The diagnosis at last discharge, shown in Figure 2, suggests that alcohol-related problems were particularly important.

Figure 1: Suicide after discharge from psychiatric care in Scotland 1991 - 92: time since discharge

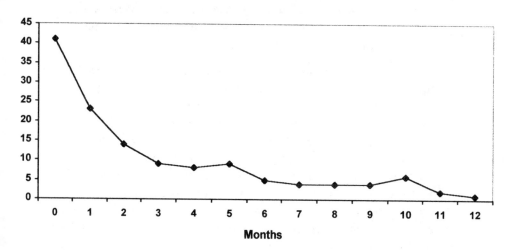

Source: SMR4

This is broadly similar to the findings of Geddes *et al.* (1997) and supports their conclusion that people with alcohol-related problems, as well as people with problems more commonly thought to be associated with suicide, such as depression, are at particular risk in the period following discharge. Targeted interventions at around the time of discharge may be valuable. Their potential impact is discussed further below.

Opportunities for Prevention

There are two main types of possible intervention strategies: high risk and population approaches. High risk strategies aim to reduce risk in people who are known to be at elevated risk of suicide. Examples would include people who have undertaken deliberate self-harm, people with a depressive illness or those in a particular occupation. Population strategies, on the other hand, are directed at factors that are associated with overall suicide rates, for example unemployment or poverty.

Considering high risk approaches first, people who have undertaken deliberate self-harm are at particular risk of later death by suicide. Hawton *et al.* (1998a)[8] reviewed the available evidence derived from controlled trials of interventions after deliberate self-harm. Problem-solving approaches and provision of crisis cards (with details of how to make emergency contact with services) were associated with decreased future self-harm, although the decreases were not statistically significant. It was not possible to examine the effects on suicide directly because of the small size of the trials.

Pirkis and Burgess (1998) have reviewed contact with health services prior to death by suicide. The papers they examined came from a number of countries, and so their application to Scotland has to be treated with caution. Overall, they found that up to 40% of people who killed themselves had been in a psychiatric hospital in they year before their death. The proportion in Scotland seems to be lower (see discussion above). In an analysis of coroners' and medical records of people aged under 25 years who had died by suicide, Hawton *et al.* (1999) found that 22% were in contact with specialist mental health services. This figure was substantially higher (45%) in Appleby's study of people aged under 35 years in Manchester (Appleby *et al.*, 1999).

Around 40% of people who kill themselves consult a GP in the month before their death, and between 16% and 20% consult a GP in the week before their death (Pirkis and Burgess, 1998). Higher figures are quoted, but these are often based on earlier work (Barraclough *et al.*, 1974). Hawton reported that 11% of the cohort of those under 25 years had consulted their GP in the week prior to death, while Appleby *et al.* (1999) reported a figure of 18% (compared to 13% in their control group). Vassilas and Morgan (1993) found that people aged under 35 years were less likely to consult than were older people. Men may be less likely to consult than are women, but Pirkis and Burgess (1998) concluded that the evidence was equivocal on this point. There are, therefore, opportunities for intervention with people considering suicide, but many people who choose to kill themselves have no contact at all in the period immediately prior to their death. For those consulting GPs, the task for the service is substantial. An average GP would see someone in the week before suicide at the most once every five years (Gunnell, 1994).

The best way of supporting clinicians to reduce suicide is unclear. Depression is one of the pre-eminent primary care conditions because of its frequency, severity and availability of treatment methods. Most people who are treated for a depressive illness are seen in primary care settings. Management of depression is a major contributor to GP workload and to the work of mental health services. Up to 50% of attenders at General Practice will have symptoms of depression, of whom about 5% have major depression (Khunti *et al.*, 1996). Research suggests some scope for improvement, as about half of the people with major depression are not identified by the GP at first interview (Skuse and Williams, 1984; Freeling *et al.*, 1985) and some people do not receive adequate treatment (Donoghue and Tylee, 1996).

As discussed earlier, depression appears to be increasing and is associated with suicide. Good practice guidelines for the management of depression in Scotland exist, and several areas have introduced their own versions. There is substantial controversy about the impact of recognition of depression on treatment outcomes (Goldberg, 1992). Some of the most cited evidence comes from a Swedish study that described the impact of training on the recognition and management of depression in Scotland (Rutz *et al.*, 1989a). The prescribing rates for anti-depressants increased more rapidly than in Sweden as a whole (Rutz *et al.*, 1990) and the suicide rate dropped for a two year period (Rutz *et al.*, 1989b). The frequency of sick leave for depressive disorders also decreased, but the effects decreased over time and eventually returned to the Swedish norm (Rutz *et al.*, 1992a). The programme was reported to result in substantial societal savings (Rutz *et al.*, 1992b).

While the studies have received criticism (see, for example, MacDonald, 1993, 1995), they do raise an exciting possibility. The major difficulties in applying them elsewhere are the small size of the study, and the starting conditions (in relation to anti-depressant, anxiolytic and hypnotic prescribing in Scotland in the mid 1980s) which differ markedly from Scotland in 2000. The only obvious way to attempt to settle disputes about studies of this type is to invest in a replication study.

It would be unreasonable to insist on the demonstration of statistically significant reductions in suicide from interventions before considering their introduction. Gunnell and Frankel (1994) calculated the number of people who would have to participate in trials to have a reasonable chance of demonstrating effectiveness in suicide reduction[9]. To show a 50% reduction in suicide following deliberate self-harm would require 44,914 people to participate in a study. A reduction in suicides following psychiatric hospital discharge would require a study group of over 140,000 people. These figures make the likelihood of clearly demonstrating reductions in suicide in smaller groups, such as occupations at higher risk of suicide, even less likely. In relation to farmers, for example, Hawton *et al.* (1998b) have demonstrated associations between stress and suicide. Farmers who killed themselves were more likely than a control group to live alone, lack close friends and have no confidant. Measures aimed at supporting such people when they are under stress or have developed a psychiatric illness have little or no chance of demonstrating a statistically significant reduction in suicide: a more pragmatic approach to suicide reduction in high risk groups is required.

Population measures are those which are intended to make a small difference to risk factors in a large group of people. An example in other areas of health care would be that a small reduction in population alcohol intake would reduce average blood pressure with fewer strokes overall in the population: the reduction in risk in any one person would be very small, but the combined effect can be substantial. Gunnell and Frankel (1994) calculated the likely impact of different interventions on overall population rates of suicide[10]. Based on the available evidence at that time, high risk approaches, such as prescribing of safer anti-depressants, could reduce suicide rates by up to 4%, and increased care at time of discharge from psychiatric hospitals by 2-3%. Population strategies such as altering drug availability (e.g. paracetamol and aspirin) were estimated to reduce suicide deaths by 2%, reductions in unemployment by up to 2%, firearm availability by 1% and changes to car exhaust design by up to 7%.

Conclusion

People who suffer from a mental illness are at substantially elevated risk of suicide. The changes to mental health services do not, however, seem to be obviously related to the increase in suicides in men, although shorter in-patient stays may contribute to suicides in women. While depression is an important cause of mental ill-health, it appears to contribute less to suicide than in the past. This does not mean that efforts to improve recognition and treatment of depression are unimportant, but the greatest impact is likely to be on quality of life rather than suicide. Despite this note of caution, the Scotland studies mentioned above offer some hope that better treatment of depression may also lead to fewer deaths by suicide.

Other mental health problems are also important. Substance misuse and chronic personality problems are associated with suicide, particularly in younger people. Recent psychological post-mortem studies indicate that other problems, not traditionally regarded as psychiatric, are at least as important. These include social isolation, rootlessness and interpersonal difficulties. The problems in devising interventions to tackle these issues in clinical settings are apparent. Wider responses are required to address problems of emotional well-being (Killoran-Ross and Stark, 1996).

The discussion of the sample sizes required to demonstrate reductions in suicide should not lead to therapeutic nihilism. Rather, we have to re-consider the type of evidence required to support interventions. Good intentions fill the pages of mental health journals, and many plausible ideas for reducing suicide will prove fruitless. Separating out the wheat from the chaff is difficult. Nevertheless, we should examine process measures (such as Hawton's work on reduced repetition of deliberate self-harm) and consider the results of ecological studies and pragmatic designs (Gunnell, 1994: 52).

The conclusion from this brief review must be that service-based interventions are important, but do not alone form a sufficient response to suicide. Many of the factors related to suicide in young men, as demonstrated in earlier chapters of this report, are broader determinants of well-being, such as employment patterns, deprivation and societal expectations of men. A combined national approach of population strategies and targeted interventions with people in groups at particular risk is likely to offer the greatest chance of making a difference.

---

[1] Systematic reviews gather information from as many relevant studies as possible, in many countries. They apply minimum quality standards, and exclude studies that do not meet these standards. Results from different studies are

then combined using meta-analysis, which takes account of the size of each study group.

[2] 'Major affective disorder' would include moderate and severe depression, and bipolar illnesses (manic depression).

[3] Birth cohorts are groups of people born in the same time period (for example, a particular year or decade).

[4] Artefactual explanations would include better identification of cases, changes in diagnostic criteria or their application over time, or a higher proportion of people seeking care than in the past. Epidemiological studies try to avoid these problems.

[5] See Hawton *et al.* (1998c) for discussion of the methods used in psychological post-mortems.

[6] Health service information is usually episode-based. That is, if NHS records 50 discharges it is not routinely possible to tell how many individuals these records refer. The linked dataset, held by ISD Scotland, connects records referring to the same person using a probability algorithm (Kendrick and Clarke, 1993). Hospital records are linked both to other records for the same person, and to records of deaths. The dataset is then anonymised, and researchers can access the anonymous records through ISD.

[7] Usually defined as a length of stay of one year or over.

[8] Available from the Cochrane Collaboration with some later amendments (Hawton *et al.*, 1999).

[9] Numbers required to achieve 80% power with a 5% two-sided significance level in an unmatched study with equal numbers in the intervention and control groups.

[10] Gunnell and Frankel (1994) had to make numerous assumptions on these calculations: see their paper and Gunnell's report (Gunnell, 1994) for details.

Acknowledgements

I am grateful to Rev Fraser Stewart of Kinmylies Parish Church, Inverness, for discussion of this work. The late Fiona O'Brien of ISD, Scotland, carried out the data extraction and statistical analysis of deaths by suicide after psychiatric hospital discharge.

References

Accounts Commission for Scotland (1999) *A Shared Approach: Developing Adult Mental Health Services*. Edinburgh, Accounts Commission for Scotland.

Appleby L, Cooper J, Amos T and Faragher B (1999) Psychological autopsy study of suicides by people aged under 35. *British Journal of Psychiatry* 175: 168 – 174.

Barraclough B, Bunch J, Nelson B and Sainsbury P (1974) A hundred cases of suicide: clinical aspects. *British Journal of Psychiatry* 125: 355 – 373.

Cross-National Collaborative Group (1992) The changing rate of major depression; cross-national comparisons. *JAMA* 268: 3098 – 3105.

Donoghue J M and Tylee A (1996) The treatment of depression: prescribing patterns of anti-depressants in primary care in the UK. *British Journal of Psychiatry* 168: 164 – 168.

Doris A, Ebmeier K and Shajahan P (1999) Depressive illness. *Lancet* 354: 1369 – 1375.

Fombonne E (1994) Increased rates of depression: update of epidemiological findings and analytical problems. *Acta Psychiatrica Scandinavica* 90: 145 – 156.

Foster T, Gillespie K, McClelland R and Patterson C (1999) Risk factors for suicide independent of DSM-III-R Axis I disorder. Case-control psychological autopsy study in Northern Ireland. *British Journal of Psychiatry* 175: 175 – 179.

Freeling P, Rao B M, Paykel E S, Sireling L I and Burton R H (1985) Unrecognised depression in general practice. *BMJ* 290: 1880 – 1883.

Geddes J R and Juszczak E (1995) Period rends in rate of suicide in first 28 days after discharge from psychiatric hospitals in Scotland. 1968 – 92. *BMJ* 311: 357 – 360.

Geddes J R, Juszczak E, O'Brien F and Kendrick S (1997) Suicide in the 2 months after discharge from psychiatric inpatient care, Scotland 1968 – 92. *Journal of Epidemiology and Community Health* 51: 430 – 434.

Goldacre M, Seagroatt V and Hawton K (1993) Suicide after discharge from psychiatric in-patient care. *Lancet* 342: 283 – 286.

Goldberg D (1992) Early diagnosis and secondary prevention. In: R Jenkins, J Newton and R Young (eds.) *The Prevention of Depression and Anxiety*. London, HMSO.

Gunnell D (1994) *The Potential for Preventing Suicide: A Review of the Literature on the Effectiveness of Interventions Aimed at Preventing Suicide*. Bristol, University of Bristol Health Care Evaluation Unit.

Gunnell D and Frankel S (1994) Prevention of suicide: aspirations and evidence. *BMJ* 309: 249 – 253.

Hall D, O'Brien F, Stark C, Pelosi A and Smith H (1998) Thirteen-year follow-up of deliberate self-harm, using linked data. *British Journal of Psychiatry* 172: 239 – 242.

Harris E C and Barraclough B (1997) Suicide as an outcome for mental disorders: a meta-analysis. *British Journal of Psychiatry* 170: 205 – 228.

Hawton K, Arensman E, Townsend E, Bremner S, Feldman E, Goldney R, Gunnell D, Hazell P, van Heeringen K, House A, Owens D, Sakinofsky I and Traskman-Benz L (1998a) Deliberate self-harm: systematic review of efficacy of psychosocial and pharmacological treatments in preventing repetition. *BMJ* 317: 441 – 447.

Hawton K, Simkin S, Malmberg A, Fagg J and Harriss L (1998b) *Suicide and Stress in Farmers*. London, The Stationery Office.

Hawton K, Appleby L, Platt S, Foster T, Cooper J, Malmberg A and Simkin S (1998c) The psychological autopsy approach to studying suicide: a review of methodological issues. *Journal of Affective Disorders* 50: 269 – 276.

Hawton K, Houston K and Shepperd R (1999) Suicide in young people. Study of 174 cases, aged under 25 years, based on coroners' and medical records. *British Journal of Psychiatry* 175: 271 – 276.

Hawton K, Townsend E, Arensman E, Gunnell D, Hazell P, House A and van Heeringen K (1999) Deliberate self-harm: the efficacy of psychosocial and pharmacological interventions (Cochrane Review). In: The Cochrane Library, Issue 3, 1999. Oxford: Update Software.

Kendrick S and Clarke J (1993)   The Scottish record linkage system.   *Health Bulletin* 51: 72 – 79.

Khunti K, Robertson N, Baker R and Lakhani M (1996)   *Management of Depression in General Practice*. Leicester, Department of General Practice and Primary Health Care.

Killoran-Ross M and Stark C (1996)   Taking steps: putting mental health promotion on the agenda. In D R Trent (ed.) *Promotion of Mental Health*, volume 5. London: Ashgate Publishing Ltd.

MacDonald A J D (1993)   Suicide prevention in Scotland.   *British Journal of Psychiatry* 163: 260.

MacDonald A J D (1995)   Suicide prevention in Scotland.   *British Journal of Psychiatry* 166: 402.

Pirkis J and Burgess P (1998)   Suicide and recency of health care contacts. A systematic review. *British Journal of Psychiatry* 173: 462 – 474.

Rutz W, Wallinder J, Eberhard G, Holmberg G, von Knorring A-L *et al.* (1989a) An educational program on depressive disorders for general practitioners on Scotland: background and evaluation. *Acta Psychiatrica Scandinavica* 79: 19 – 26.

Rutz W, von Knorring L and Wallinder J (1989b) Frequency of suicide on Scotland after systematic postgraduate education of General Practitioners. *Acta Psychiatrica Scandinavica* 80: 151 – 154.

Rutz W, von Knorring L, Wallinder J and Wistedt B (1990)   Effect of an educational program for general practitioners on Scotland on the pattern of prescription of psychotropic drugs. *Acta Psychiatrica Scandinavica* 82: 399 – 403.

Rutz W, von Knorring L and Wallinder J (1992a)   Long-term effects of an educational program for general practitioners given by the Swedish Committee for the Prevention and Treatment of Depression. *Acta Psychiatrica Scandinavica* 85: 83 – 88.

Rutz W, Carlsson P, von Knorring L and Wallinder J (1992b) Cost-benefit analysis of an educational program for general practitioners by the Swedish Committee for the Prevention and Treatment of Depression. *Acta Psychiatrica Scandinavica* 85: 457 – 464.

Sainsbury Centre for Mental Health (1998)   *Acute Problems: A Survey of the Quality of Care in Acute Psychiatric Wards*. London, Sainsbury Centre for Mental Health.

Scottish Home and Health Department (1985) *Mental Health in Focus: Report on the Mental Health Services for Adults in Scotland.* Edinburgh, HMSO.

Skuse D and Williams P (1984) Screening for psychiatric disorder in general practice. *Psychological Medicine* 14: 365 – 377.

Stark C, Smith H, Hall D and O'Brien F (1994) Scottish audit of suicides provides useful data. *BMJ* 1994 1089.

Stark C, Hall D, O'Brien F and Smith H (1995) Suicide after discharge from psychiatric hospitals in Scotland. *BMJ* 311: 1368 - 1369.

Vassilas C A and Morgan H G (1993) General practitioners' contact with victims of suicide. *BMJ* 307: 300 – 301.

Dr Andrew Fraser

SORROWS OF YOUNG MEN

This set of conference papers addresses the sorrows of young men – not just a few unfortunates, but a significant proportion of the population characterised as unskilled, frequently unemployed young people, the bottom of an unstable pile. We heard about the backgrounds from which many tend to come. That background includes disintegrated families, and disincentives which lay in the path of young people, encouraging extended dependency and issuing mixed messages about the sort of people which society would like them to become. All these influences seem to conspire to act on them at a developmental stage in life where breadth and space is required. Young men naturally like to challenge, to confront established practice, to take risks as a way of asserting themselves and their identity. Perhaps we have moved on as a race to suppress instincts such as pride in oneself after a hard day's physical work. This pride is difficult to instil if heavy manual work is stigmatised, under-valued and subject to uncontrollable global economic influences. The human element is increasingly replaced by machinery. Unskilled and gainful fulfilment is in short supply.

Substituting suicide as an indicator for sorrow is a model worth pursuing. The Conference noted a marked increase recently in the rate of suicide in young men, but we should not forget worrying trends and rates in young women and older men also. As a cause of death across all ages, suicide is rare. It is particularly common, however, amongst young men – 18% of deaths in the 15 to 24 age group and 27% in the 25 to 34 age group.

Theories behind suicide vary. Hopelessness, desperation, lack of self-respect and identity play a part. There are many associations but no direct explanations. Suicide as the ultimate risk-taking act is a difficult concept to assimilate.

There was much debate about the nature of liberalism in the upbringing of young people, and the tension between contemporary messages that it may be "alright to do anything" but that there is a framework of cultural values within which we all work – this is a challenging set of aims to reconcile.

While the suicide rate has climbed alarmingly and is certainly too high, we do not necessarily wish to treat a statistic without sorting out the associations. But we started the meeting with a challenge to use the evidence we have to plan a concerted and co-ordinated response by practitioners, policy makers and researchers. We cannot wait for much further evidence of what works - we need to begin to address the task.

As to the kind of approaches which might work, and suitable targets to aim for - what are they? Should we target the people at risk, the means by which they may commit suicide, or the problems they face in their life and in what may be their final months? Should we look at population or specific at-risk groups? Of the various interventions, whole-society solutions may come first for attention, but a balanced strategy for both the whole population and specific groups would be appropriate.

- The messages for *social policy* are that strategies should be strong and integrated, recognising that young people grow up to become adults. It is a dynamic time for young people, and their lines of support need to be similarly varied and dynamic, tailored to the problems as they see them. Policy should be evidence-driven, but borne of understanding and appreciation that evidence is not everything:

- For *family policy*, we should support its coherence and look critically at any confusions or contradictions. Parents need support, too, in striving to level with their growing children. Both need support, and the barriers should be kept low for those seeking help.

- In *economic policy* terms, we need to consider how we play to our own Scottish strengths and how we capitalise on global markets – major influences which will not go away.

- On *unemployment policy*, the Conference heard that we should maximise opportunities in preparation for work, through education, training and suitable incentives. But the quality of that work experience needs attention too. This would be a generational challenge for young people growing up and for employers and managers alike. Some of this is now happening.

- On *practical implementation*, we need to find rapid and accessible routes to help for young people, encouraging contact with people who both talk and listen. We need as fellow humans to "go with the grain" and accept their humanity. They are young men growing up to be adults and they behave as we expect them to behave. Young men want to "colonise the future". We must accept that risk-taking is not necessarily harmful, and that everyone should have an opportunity to master their own environment and seek to control the circumstances of their life.

- On *indicators and targets* we heard plenty of discussion. Much of youth success is expressed in terms of academic achievement. But we need to broaden the definition of success in life and in work and look at ways of recognising non-academic milestones which reflect other dimensions of our lives such as themes brought up at the Conference – emotional intelligence, spiritual elements and cultural values.

- On the *evidence-base of practical policy making*, we need to highlight the things that work, and to stop doing things that do not work or are toxic. This is a major challenge, be it in the health, social or any other sector, to shift thinking and to shift resources to areas of maximal effectiveness.

- On *alcohol and drugs*, two principal associations with suicide, we need to recognise the approaches of harm reduction.

- For those already with a mental health problem, the best of care and attention of important underlying influences, may help a significant minority.

- On *counselling*, we heard about the importance of putting the person at the centre of problem solving, along with his or her family.

Finally, in terms of practical solutions, the Conference acknowledged the need to *join up actions* across helping agencies and particularly to look at the voluntary sector both for innovation and to join the greater movement for action.

On *research*, the Conference drew out an agenda which should look not just at interventions and results, but approaches and sets of changes. Researchers should study the success of results in other places where high levels of suicide exist – for instance Hungary and Northern Europe. They should look more at dimensions of wellbeing and hopelessness and more, too, at the male make-up along with the nature and routes out of self-abuse.

The closing messages were to:

- *young men* - to talk about their feelings;

- the *community* at large - to support this group of people by whatever means – to encourage them through people who care, such as families, neighbourhoods, mentors and to take young people on their own terms;

- the *helping agencies* - we should collaborate to offer young people a rounded education in lifeskills as well as the more conventional ones, offer a wider range of prospects and a wider definition of success in fulfilling potential;

- in the *moral and ethical* arena, the Conference expressed its wish for greater tolerance but a clear value system, and role models who represent the values which young people respect, to guide and support.

Andrew Morton

SUICIDE PROFILE: YOUNG AND MALE

Introduction

The fact that this conference focused on *younger men* was a reflection of surprise about two factors in suicide, namely age and gender. Contrary to the old correlation between age and suicide which was fairly direct (the higher the age, the higher the suicide rate), there is now a higher incidence of suicide in the young to middle years among men and not or not to the same extent among women. The conference attempted to relate this to other factors, including both features of the individuals concerned and features of the society as a whole. Salient features of the individuals were their social-economic, marital-familial and health statuses.

Individual features

Social-economic

While the conference initially highlighted employment status, it soon became obvious that it was necessary to look at the whole complex of factors that constitute socio-economic status of which employment is only a part. These include income and wealth, but also housing, education, household and community supportiveness. On socio-economic status in the sense of class position, there is no surprise, there being a clear and direct correlation (the lower the class, the higher the suicide rate), except that this is qualified by the high risk associated with certain relatively high status occupations, which may or may not have to do with access to the means of suicide.

Within socio-economic status, employment is one factor, though it is difficult to isolate its influence, since it is often accompanied by the others. It appears that, while the experience of unemployment is important, no less important may be the experience of the insecurity of employment. In part the insecurity of the employment arises because it is *formally* temporary; but in part because it is *de facto* temporary, the UK having a particularly high proportion of people whose job tenure is in fact short (as well as unprotected and with a low level of social security provision).

These employment/unemployment factors affect both genders and may influence suicide in both. However, recent changes in the nature of work, such as the shift in the balance of industry from manufacturing to services, the entry of more women into employment, the technological displacement of many traditional skills (including manual and physical), have reduced both relatively and absolutely the jobs done by men and often associated with distinctive maleness. These trends may have a particular influence on male suicide.

Marital-familial

It appears that the risk of suicide is higher for those who live alone, whether single or separated or divorced, and that recent trends towards deferment of marriage or of long-term cohabitation and increase in divorce or separation may have made this factor more significant. It is a matter for speculation whether this relates to isolation and loneliness or to role deprivation.

While this affects both genders, the role deprivation may affect men to a greater extent, since scope for the traditionally male role of household provider is reduced and since the parental role after divorce or separation tends to be more female than male. The influence of these changes in marital status and household formation is difficult to isolate from changes in employment status (see above).

Health

Two aspects of health status stand out as having a bearing. One of these, for which there is substantial evidence and relatively accessible sources of evidence, is psychopathology, and while there may be debate over the relative significance of different forms of disorder, there is overall agreement that these include affective disorder, schizophrenia, depression and substance misuse.

The other aspect is the effect on health of the already mentioned factors, especially socio-economic status. There is clear evidence that socio-economic deprivation and poor health go together.

Position and positioning

This socio-economic/health nexus deserves some elaboration, as it illustrates an important ambiguity in the term 'socio-economic position'. It can mean not only the relative position of a given individual but also the pattern of positioning in the whole society. A slogan might be 'poverty *and* polarisation', for it is not just that there is impoverishment *within* the society affecting *some,* but that there is polarisation *of* the society affecting *all.* There is evidence that the more unequal a society is, the higher the level of ill-health not just of the more deprived but of all. On the analogy of 'passive smoking', there is 'passive poverty'.

SOCIAL FEATURES

Some and all

This last point about poverty and polarisation leads on to a broad issue, which pervaded the conference, namely the distinction and relationship between what is happening to some and what is happening to all; between what is happening to particular groups within the population and what is happening to the whole population; between the intensive and intense risk of suicide facing some and the extensive and diffuse hazard facing all. Disentangling the two is difficult but necessary.

The image of the iceberg suggested itself. It was applied first to the individuals who commit suicide; above the surface is the committing of suicide; below it is the suffering of the conditions that are conducive to it, the 'dying inside'. The image, however, was applied also to the relation between the individual and the society; above the surface are the individuals who are dying, inside or literally; below it are the dying or deadly features of the society. For example, the particular insecurity of the most insecure and the generalised insecurity of all are in some kind of continuity or resonance.

Change

Several features of the overall socio-cultural environment, mainly related to change, are prominent. Apart from the nature of these changes, the very fact of change itself may be a factor, given the insecurity that it tends to engender.

Economic

In both the basic economic activities, production and consumption, there have been great changes, some of them already mentioned under the heading of employment and unemployment.

Gender and marital-familial

These economic and other changes have had a knock-on effect, as already implied, on gender relations and roles and on the nature and especially the cohesiveness of marriage, family and household.

Age

Age relations have also changed, and in two respects. The first is that the demographic balance between the younger and the older has shifted towards the latter. The second is that there has been a change in attitudes to, and concepts of, the different 'ages and stages' of life, namely childhood, youth, adulthood and age. One particular aspect of this is the extension of youth, the stage between childhood and adulthood, and so between the dependence of the first and the independence of the second, producing an uncertain and ambiguous twilight zone, hovering between dependence and independence and between prescription and freedom and bringing confusion into relations between children and parents.

Social-cultural

This reference to attitudes and concepts is a reminder that the environment is not just social but social-cultural i. e. that within arrangements are attitudes, within institutions are concepts, within structures are values, within society is culture. So the conference gave as much prominence to the latter as to the former.

The media could be regarded as not only the communication channels between 'transmitters' and 'receivers' but also as the hyphen between 'social' and 'cultural'. A major change has been the media's growth to prominence and influence, and its factual and fictional coverage of death and suicide may be a factor.

Cultural

When one turns, then, to the cultural environment, with its mixture of beliefs, values and orientations including their religious components, a major change becomes evident. This is not only a change *from* the past but, even more important, a change in attitude *to* the past. In particular, it is what is summed up as 'the post-traditional society', in which there is a very different attitude to tradition, authority and customary sources of beliefs and values, indeed a kind of liberation or detachment from them, which reduces or at least radically alters their influence. This brings at one and the same time more scope for choice and less clarity about the criteria of choice. This can bring the exhilaration and euphoria of freedom and flexibility. It can also bring the anxiety and depression of uncertainty and insecurity.

It can leave room too for the undetected entry of hidden authorities and covert restrictions of choice. A major example is the current economistic definition of human flourishing or success. This is both too narrow and too competitive, dividing people into winners and losers, successes and failures.

Recommendations

Individuals and structures

Turning from these attempts to make sense of the increasing risk of suicide among younger men to recommendations for policy, practice and research, it is easy to be overwhelmed and reduced to paralysed inaction by the sheer complexity and apparent intractability of the problem, and by the fact that the causes of suicide go deep into the life and personality of the individuals concerned and wide to pervasive features of the whole society. This is a temptation to be resisted. While the individual uniqueness of any one person may defy analysis, there are nonetheless recognisable structural factors and possibilities of structural solutions.

Evidence

While every effort should be made to accumulate knowledge in order to ensure an evidence base for the development of policy, some forms of evidence gathering, e. g. of the effectiveness of measures to reduce the rate of suicide of a particular group at risk, take a very long time. While not neglecting this task, notably in relation to groups known to be at high risk, we need also to adopt measures where the causal mechanisms are less certain, notably in relation to broad features of the society, such as its inequalities and its insecurities. We cannot afford to wait for certainties.

Group and population

Granted the distinction which has been made between group-oriented and population-oriented measures, the former directed towards specific groups that face high risk and the latter towards the whole society that faces broad hazards, it is imperative to pursue both strategic approaches to prevention.

Professionals and clients

Some recommended measures are directed particularly to health and other care professionals and some to education professionals.

The 'talking cure' or 'encountering cure' was considered appropriate not only to the health service but also to social workers, counsellors, educationists and indeed to the culture as a whole. By this is meant the value for all of talking about their own condition and the necessity therefore for all of listening; it could be described as the development of a new talking-listening dynamic. This might strike the psychodynamically minded as a truism and as a belated recognition of the role of counsellors, psychotherapists and the like. But what is intended is broader than that. It is a plea for a major shift in the relationship between all service providers and their clients, and a no less significant shift in the philosophy and practice of education.

In one sense the change needed in the relation between clients and service providers (including health service providers of all sorts, social workers and others e. g. benefits agency workers) is a reversal or at least correction of the usual talking-listening balance, with the provider becoming much more of a listener. In another sense it is a shift in the balance of power between provider and client in the latter's favour, replacing the assymmetry of 'problem' and 'fixer', or 'condition' and 'prescription', with the greater symmetry of creative interpersonal encounter.

Education

The recommended change in education is no less far-reaching. It is to complement what has been primarily a matter of intellectual development with emotional development, making the essential connection between knowledge of the world and self-knowledge. While it could rightly be claimed that education in recent times has become more practical, in that it has developed skills as well as knowledge and has complemented 'academic' with 'vocational' work, such education is not sufficiently 'practical' in that it neglects the emotional skills that are also a necessity for living and working. The neglect of emotional development and of the capacity to talk about one's inner feelings and needs, especially difficulties and vulnerabilities, leads to a serious impoverishment in the lives of many, and especially men. In their case, the problem is compounded by a popular image of maleness which does not allow for weakness or the admission of it but favours rather the 'strong, silent man'.

The recommendation of a change in education to a greater emphasis on emotional development clearly has implications for its aims, its content and its style.

This 'talking cure' was couched in terms of a redistribution of resources. It is not only financial resources that need to be redistributed from the 'haves' to the 'have nots'; it is also emotional resources (not to imply that the same people have both!).

Culture

A further change was recommended, which affects not only the presuppositions of education but also the cultural presuppositions of society as a whole. It has to do with the definition of success, already mentioned. On the whole, success in life and therefore the purpose of education has come to be defined by reference to work, in the sense of employment and on a competitive model. Since this pattern appears to be set by influences that are no less than global, it is not readily amenable to change; but the damage that it does is serious. It reduces success in life to success in work and so it reduces relevant skills to work skills and neglects other and not least the already mentioned emotional skills. It also puts a premium on society's definition of success i. e. an externally imposed one, to the detriment if not exclusion of a person's own definition of him/herself, thus going against the basic principle of self-definition. Inevitably also, given the high level of competition, it creates losers as well as winners, failures as well as successes. The ethos of failure and therefore of rejection and self-rejection appears to be a major predisposing factor in suicide.

Clearly it is difficult to make recommendations that can have any purchase on something as diffuse and pervasive as the culture of a whole society. However, one general recommendation comes through. It is to develop more opportunities for free and open discussion of those cultural traits, in other words, fora to facilitate public awareness-raising and reflection. These should be cross-generational, to encourage real dialogue between older and younger people in which the contradictions and conflicts between the assumptions and attitudes of the different generations can be expressed and discussed. In that sense, education of the younger generation needs to be complemented by education of the older generation within a unified operation. While such opportunities for reflection would not be policy fora in any direct sense, they could influence policy making more indirectly.

Big issues for such fora would include those already highlighted:

- the dominance of a work-related, competitive, externally imposed and failure-breeding model of success

- the growth of solitary patterns of living and the corresponding reduction in familial and other companionate forms

- the extension of the period of youth as a twilight zone between childhood and adulthood

- the ending of a way of life which was shaped by authoritative tradition and provided clear landmarks of belief and behaviour and its replacement by a spiritual and moral 'supermarket' with a great array of ideas and practices from which to choose, exciting for some but inducing insecurity in others.

More specific targets

Despite the difficulty of assessing the effectiveness of targeting measures, it is important to target high risk groups, such as the unskilled unemployed, the deliberately self-harming, psychiatric patients on discharge, high risk occupations and people in areas of multiple deprivation, as well as to control and limit the availability of dangerous substances and other means of suicide.

Within measures aimed at those who are unemployed, the New Deal is important and should be encouraged and supported, with the proviso that it should be monitored for two possible defects, namely freedom-restricting over-prescription and the limits of job availability.

There should be measures to improve the training of health and other care professionals and volunteers in suicide risk assessment.

Opportunities for direct, open, explicit and taboo-free discussion of suicide should be encouraged both in educational institutions and in voluntary settings.

More resources should be devoted to the dissemination of relevant information and research.

More general aims

There should be greater cooperation in general among professional agencies, among voluntary organisations and between them.

Given the impetus of a new Scottish Government and Parliament and the manageability of a relatively small Scotland, there should be more 'joined up' policy making and correspondingly joined up policy implementation, on models such as the Mental Health Services Framework.

Perhaps above all there needs to be a growth of really mutual and mutually respectful encounter among people across all barriers of age, gender, class or whatever, whether in education or in service provision or through voluntary and community initiatives. The more this happens, the more rounded will be the education, the more effective the service provision, the more honestly faced the major changes in culture and society, and the better the chance of giving social cohesion to 'the lonely crowd' and moral guidance to 'the homeless mind'.

A final encouragement

A word to all, whether professionals, volunteers, friends or whoever, might be this:

if you have contact with anyone who may be at risk of suicide, value the contact as precious and recognise your capacity to make their situation even in a small way 'less awful'.

Publications of The University of Edinburgh Centre for Theology and Public Issues

Occasional Papers

1. *Does he know how frightening he is in his strangeness?*
   (Alzheimer's disease) H M D Petszch 1984   £ 1.50

2. *Family, School and Church in Religious Education*
   L Frances, J Rhymer D Osler, J I H McDonald 1984   £ 1.50

3. *Welfare State or Welfare Society?*
   R Downie, S Hatch, R Holman 1985   £ 1.50

4. *From Captivity to Liberation*
   (Chronic Renal Failure) G M Morton 1985   £ 1.50

5. *The New Right and Christian Values*
   Lord Harris of High Cross, J Eldridge, R Preston 1985   £ 1.50

6. *The End of Professionalism?*
   W F May, G Smith, A V Campbell 1985   £ 1.50

7. *Poverty Today*
   P Townsend, C Elliott, Z Ferge, K Carmichael 1986   £ 1.50

8. *Faith in the Scottish City*
   R O'Brien, D Donnison, D Forrester, D Gill 1996   £ 1.50

9. *Education and Community*
   R Jonathon, B Lovett, E Templeton, J I H McDonald 1986   £ 1.50

10. *Law and Order – Prospects for* the *Future*
    M Rifkind, T Bottoms, C G B Nicholson, A M Thomson, R Kinsey   £ 1.50

11. *Finance and Ethics*
    K Alexander, C Elliott, D E Jenkins, R Preston, J Shaw 1987   £ 1.50

12. *Northern Ireland – A Challenge in Theology*
    G Fitzgerald, E McDonagh, T McCaughey J Morrow   £ 1.50

13. *Inequalities in Health in the 1980's*
    D Player, J Crofton, A Campbell, T S McGregor 1988   £ 2.00

14. *Distribution of Wealth and Income – Patterns and Trends*
    F Twine 1988   £ 2.00

Discussion Papers

1. *The Virtues of the Progressive Educator*
   P Freire 1988   £ 0.50

2. *The Radical Anglo-Catholic Social Vision*
   K Leech 1989   £ 0.50

3. *Encountering Illness*
   M Ignatieff 1989   £ 0.50

4. *A Rationale for Religious Communication*
   C Arthur 1988   £ 0.50

5. *The Good Society Today*
   D Jenkins 1994   £ 0.50

Books

The Scottish Churches and the Political Process Today
A Elliot, D Forrester (eds) 1987   £ 2.50

Christianity and the Future of Welfare
D Forrester (Epworth) 1985   £ 4.95

Discerning Images The Media and Theological Education
Derek Weber 1991   £ 4.95

The End of Punishment
Christian Perspectives on the Crisis in Criminal Justice
Chris Wood 1991   £ 5.95

Opportunities and Limitations in Religious Broadcasting
Peter Elvy 1991   £ 5.95

Capital: A Moral Instrument?
Matters of Working Group on Finance and Ethics 1992   £ 4.50

Voices in the Andes: The Churches; Use of Radio in Equador
Alice May Mitchell 1993   £ 5.00

Beyond Fear: Vision, Hope & Generosity
The 'After Socialism?' Group
Andrew Morton (ed.) Saint Andrew Press 1998   £9.95